MW01094186

Michael Faraday's
The Chemical History
of a Candle

with Guides to Lectures, Teaching Guides
& Student Activities

Other Books by the Authors

Why Engineers Need to Grow a Long Tail
Bill Hammack • 2011

How Engineers Create the World
Bill Hammack • 2011

Eight Amazing Engineering Stories
Bill Hammack, Patrick Ryan, & Nick Ziech • 2012

Albert Michelson's Harmonic Analyzer
Bill Hammack, Steve Kranz, & Bruce Carpenter • 2014

World of Chemistry, 3e
Zumdahl, S.S, Zumdahl, S.L, & DeCoste, D.J. • 2013

Introductory Chemistry, 8e
Zumdahl, S.S., & DeCoste, D.J. • 2015

Chemical Principles, 8e
Zumdahl, S.S., & DeCoste, D.J. • 2016

Chemistry, 10e
Zumdahl, S.S., Zumdahl, S.A., & DeCoste, D.J. • 2017

Michael Faraday's
The Chemical History
of a Candle

with Guides to Lectures, Teaching Guides
& Student Activities

Bill Hammack & Don DeCoste

Copyright © 2016 William S. Hammack & Donald J. DeCoste

All rights reserved. No part of this book may be reproduced in any form by any electronic or mechanical means (including photocopying, recording, or information storage and retrieval) without permission from the publisher. The contents of the book may be used freely by teachers or students without further permission, including printing the teaching guides and student activities.

Articulate Noise Books

Urbana, Illinois

First Edition: May 2016

Faraday, Michael, William S. Hammack, Donald J. DeCoste

Michael Faraday's The Chemical History of a Candle: with Guides to Lectures, Teaching Guides & Student Activities / Bill Hammack - 1ST edition (version 1.1)

ISBN 978-1-945441-00-4 (pbk)

ISBN 978-0-9839661-9-7 (electronic)

ISBN 978-0-9839661-8-0 (hbk)

1. Chemistry—Popular works. 2. Combustion—Popular works. 3. Candles. 4. Faraday, Michael, 1791–1867 I. Title.

CONTENTS

LECTURES

Preface • vii

Introduction • 1

ESSENTIAL BACKGROUND
How a Candle Works • 5

A Note on the Text of the Lectures • 11

Guide to Lecture One • 13

LECTURE ONE
A Candle: Sources of its Flame • 21

Guide to Lecture Two • 31

LECTURE TWO
Brightness of the Flame • 41

Guide to Lecture Three • 51

LECTURE THREE
Products of Combustion • 59

Guide to Lecture Four • 71

LECTURE FOUR
The Nature of the Atmosphere • 81

Guide to Lecture Five • 95

LECTURE FIVE
Respiration & its Analogy
to the Burning of a Candle • 109

TEACHING GUIDE

A Note on the Teaching Guide • 123

The Big Ideas of Chemistry:
The particulate nature of matter • 125

Observations of a Candle • 137
Teacher's Guide • 141

Convection Currents & Density • 147
Teacher's Guide • 151

Capillary Action • 155
Teacher's Guide • 159

Molecules are "Sticky" • 161
Teacher's Guide • 167

Physical Changes: Changes of State • 171
Teacher's Guide • 179

Chemical Changes • 183
Teacher's Guide • 185

Two Demonstrations to Show
the Pressure Caused by Air • 187

PREFACE

In this companion book to our video series we present Michael Faraday's great nineteenth-century lecture series *The Chemical History of a Candle*. Our goal with the videos and this book is to bring the lectures to a modern audience. We considered updating them, perhaps by rewriting the lectures in today's language, or adding in an atomic perspective. Yet, as we worked our way through the lectures we realized that non-quantum chemistry remains a great way to demonstrate the nature of science—Faraday's lectures are really an extended illustration of the scientific method. Also, as we studied the lectures, Faraday's poetic language charmed us. So, when editing the lectures, we retained most of the original language, changing it only when necessary. In addition to keeping Faraday's nineteenth-century language, we used, in the videos, modern dress and contemporary scientific apparatus.

While the book stands alone, we encourage readers to watch our video series of the lectures at *www.engineerguy.com/faraday*. This series was created with Alex Black, who was then a University of Illinois undergraduate student studying chemistry. It was produced with support from the Special Grants Program of the Dreyfus Foundation, from a Public Engagement Grant from the University of Illinois-Urbana, and from the Department of Chemical and Biomolecular Engineering.

Bill Hammack & Don DeCoste

INTRODUCTION

In the second quarter of the nineteenth century Michael Faraday (1791–1867) revolutionized our understanding of electrical phenomena. His impact on our world today is tremendous: it led to the lights in our streets and houses, electrical motors that run our appliances, and the electro-chemical processes that refine materials used to make the consumer goods we buy. Beyond this body of pioneering research, Faraday left an educational legacy: his great lectures on the "Chemical History of a Candle."

History of the lectures

Faraday presented this series of six lectures three times. Each time he began a few days after Christmas and concluded in the second week of January. For this reason they are often called the "Christmas Lectures," although their content has nothing to do with that holiday. He presented the lectures in December 1848, 1854, and 1860. A ticket to these lectures was highly prized, even for Faraday: "I am sorry," he wrote to a friend, that "I cannot supply Mr. Hadgetts with a ticket for my lectures." He entitled the lectures *A course of six lectures, adapted to a juvenile auditory, on the chemical history of a candle.* The term *juvenile* to Faraday meant what we call young adults—aged fifteen to twenty. In 1860–1861, the last time he delivered the lectures, 700 people attended. At the lectures the audience sat in tiered seating arranged in a semi-circle around Faraday. He lectured from a shallow well, behind a large table with a semi-circular opening cut out so that he could reach his demonstrations—each laid out carefully by him before the lecture. One attendee recalls Faraday's "silvery hair," his "earnest face," and his "irresistible eloquence, which compelled attention." We know the exact words Faraday used because the 1860 lectures were, as their subtitle notes, "recorded verbatim by special permission." It is this version that we edited for this edition of the lectures.

Purpose of the lectures

Faraday opens his lectures with the hope that he "shall not disappoint" by choosing the candle as a topic of investigation "rather than any newer topic, which could not be better, were it even so good." Although the roots of Faraday's lectures lie in nineteenth-century science and so neglect atomic-level description,[1] the lectures brilliantly introduce viewers to the nature of science—to the scientific method. Even now, over 150 years later, one would be hard pressed to find an object of study that would equal the candle.

Faraday justifies his choice by claiming that "there is no better, there is no more open door by which you can enter into the study of science than by considering the physical phenomena of a candle." His lectures bear out his claim: through the burning of a candle Faraday introduces listeners to the concepts of mass, density, heat conduction, capillary action, and convection currents. He highlights the difference between chemical and physical processes, such as melting, vaporization, incandescence, and all types of combustion. And, by trapping the products of the candle, Faraday reveals the nature of gases; he shows especially the properties of hydrogen, oxygen, nitrogen, and carbon dioxide, including their relative masses and the makeup of the atmosphere. He wraps up his lectures with a grand, and startling, analogy: by understanding the chemical behavior of a candle, he claims, the listener can now grasp the basics of respiration, an essential action of humans and other mammals.

A candle, Faraday notes, takes oxygen from the air, combines it with the carbon in the candle wax, and these form carbon dioxide and water. Humans effect this same chemical reaction when they breathe: oxygen inhaled with air combines with carbon-containing food to produce carbon dioxide and water, which are then exhaled. This analogy of the burning of the candle to human respiration highlights one of Faraday's great themes: how a deep understanding of fundamental science unifies the phenomena in the physical world. In addition, Faraday discusses our interrelation with the plant kingdom: while humans take in oxygen and release carbon dioxide, plants take in carbon dioxide and release oxygen; that is "what is disease to the one, is health to the other."

Notes

1. As P W Atkins noted: "Faraday knew that substances differ in the number of atoms of each element that are present ... but he would have had little conception of the patterns in which the atoms are linked together to form the molecular structure to a compound." P W Atkins *Atoms, Electrons, and Change* Scientific American Library, 1991.

HOW A CANDLE WORKS

To deeply appreciate Faraday's astonishing linking of the flicker of a candle flame to how a gasp of air enables life, a reader needs to have a clear idea of the chemistry of a burning candle. For the reader eager to tackle the lectures, we outline below, in a single paragraph, the basics of a candle's operation. A study of the more detailed events happening when a candle burns will enhance a reader's understanding of the lectures and so we've expanded on the "quick overview" with a section entitled "A detailed look at a candle."

Quick overview

When a candle is first lit the flame consumes the wick until it reaches a point just above the wax. This heat from the flame melts the wax by radiation through the air and by conduction through the wick. Only the tip of the wick burns. This liquefied wax climbs the wick to the flame by capillary action, where the molten wax is vaporized. Next, the flame burns that vapor with oxygen supplied by the surrounding air. This reaction releases gases—mainly gaseous carbon dioxide and water vapor—and heat. The heat released melts more wax, which, again, crawls up the wick and so sustains the candle's flame. A candle, then, simultaneously carries out two actions: its flame burns vaporized wax and it delivers wax to that flame to sustain it.

A detailed look at a candle

While the quick overview above highlights the important actions occurring in a candle, it is in the details that we see the complex chemical and physical process that occur. We detail below the chemical composition of the wax, the function of the wick, the chemical and physical processes in the flame, and the nature of the emissions from a candle.

Wax

Candle wax is the fuel burned by a candle. The wax is a mixture of long-chain hydrocarbons with the formula C_nH_{2n+2}. Typically the composition of the various hydrocarbons averages to $C_{25}H_{52}$. Solid candle wax will not burn, nor will molten wax: only vaporous wax burns.

The wick

The wick has two functions. First, the wick conducts heat from the flame to the solid wax. This heat melts the wax. Second, the wick transports the molten wax to the flame: the liquefied wax crawls up the wick via capillary action. The liquid rises almost to the top of the wick, where it is engulfed by flame and vaporized. Only the tip of the wick glows and it turns black as it burns. Note that the flame consumes the wick at the same rate as the solid wax of the candle is depleted.

The flame

The flame burns the vaporized wax with oxygen supplied by the surrounding air. (See figure on page 10). This reaction releases gases—mainly gaseous carbon dioxide and water vapor—and heat. The carbon dioxide is formed from carbon in the candle wax and oxygen in the air, and the water forms from hydrogen in the wax and oxygen in the air.

The flame has three regions where different chemical and physical phenomena occur. Combustion, the chemical reaction that produces carbon dioxide and water, occurs in the blue outer edge of the flame. Here the vaporized wax burns completely—*complete* means converting all the carbon in the wax to carbon dioxide rather than carbon monoxide. This region, which is the hottest part of the flame, is not uniform: the blue is concentrated at the base of the flame, and decreases toward the top of the flame, where it is only a thin layer at the flame's edge.

Combustion also occurs in the grayish-yellow section of the flame that surrounds the tip of the wick. Here the flame vaporizes the molten wax. The liquefied wax cools the flame and so this is the section of the flame with the lowest temperature. The wax here undergoes *incomplete* combustion. Incomplete combustion happens when there is not enough oxygen to combine with carbon: air, which supplies the oxygen, cannot travel easily into the flame. Because the combustion is incomplete some of the carbon from the wax remains in the flame. This darkens the flame creating the grayish cast near the wick.

These heated, solid carbon particles, glow. As they rise in the flame they create a bright yellow region. This brightest part of the flame has a temperature between that of the hot blue region and the cooler grayish-yellow region. The glowing of the carbon particles is called *incandescence*. This phenomena occurs whenever a solid is heated enough to emit light. This incandescence is a physical change, unlike combustion in other parts of the flame, which is a chemical change.

The chemical and physical changes in the flame create its distinctive shape. The flame's heat expands the surrounding air. This less dense air draws up cooler air from below the candle. These convection currents create the teardrop shape of a flame. They also sweep away the carbon dioxide and water formed. The importance of these convection currents to the candle's operation is dramatically illustrated when a candle burns in zero gravity or in a vacuum chamber.

In these environments the convection currents no longer occur and so the flame becomes spherical. The oxygen spends more time in the flame and so the combustion is more complete, i.e., more carbon is turned to carbon dioxide and fewer carbon particles exist in the flame. Because there are fewer carbon particles the flame's interior is blue. The flame burns out because, without convection currents, carbon dioxide remains in the flame and smothers it.

Emissions from the candle

A properly burning candle emits little smoke. Any smoke that arises comes from incomplete combustion in the flame: tiny particles of unburned carbon mixed with gaseous products. This smoke will "soot" a piece of metal or glass placed in the smoke well above the flame. The amount of this black smoke, then, depends on the ratio of incomplete to complete combustion. A breeze, for example, can increase the amount of incomplete combustion and cause a candle to emit black smoke. In contrast, the smoke is white and heavy when the flame is extinguished. This white smoke is vaporized wax that has formed into droplets of molten wax. If ignited with a match this stream of wax can relight the wick as demonstrated in Faraday's first lecture.

Convection air currents sweep away CO_2 and H_2O

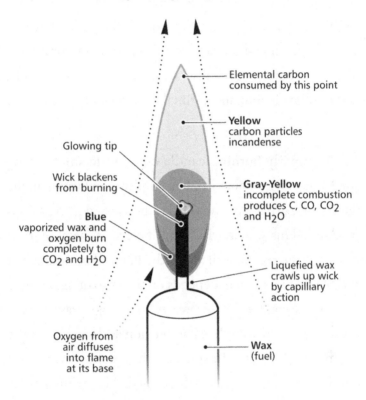

Elemental carbon consumed by this point

Yellow carbon particles incandense

Glowing tip

Wick blackens from burning

Gray-Yellow incomplete combustion produces C, CO, CO_2 and H_2O

Blue vaporized wax and oxygen burn completely to CO_2 and H_2O

Liquefied wax crawls up wick by capilliary action

Oxygen from air diffuses into flame at its base

Wax (fuel)

As Faraday notes in his first lecture "there is not a law under which any part of the universe is governed which does not come into play, and is touched upon in the chemistry of a candle." Heat from the flame melts the wax by radiation and conduction, capillary action draws the wax up the wick, molten wax is vaporized, chemical reactions produce the flame, heated solid carbon particles glow, and convection currents sweep away the products of combustion. The balanced chemical equation for the complete combustion of a candle is represented by:

$$C_{25}H_{52}(s) + 38O_2(g) \rightarrow 25CO_2(g) + 26H_2O(g)$$

A NOTE ON THE TEXT OF THE LECTURES

In editing Faraday's lectures for a modern reader we occasionally modified the original text. We updated terminology, especially chemical terms. We replaced some demonstrations with modern or safer ones. And we removed some redundant demonstrations: Faraday often demonstrated the same concept to his audiences and although that repetition worked well in a lecture hall, it seemed unnecessary in a format where one can watch again. Also, we removed from Lecture One Faraday's long description of nineteenth-century candles and candlemaking. Our largest change was to reduce the number of lectures: we condensed Faraday's six lectures to five by combining Faraday's Lectures Three and Four. We removed his demonstration of generating hydrogen from "philosopher's wool," and we replaced his "voltaic pile," which he described at length, with a DC power source.

To help the modern reader each lecture is preceded by a short guide written in contemporary language. These guides mirror the lectures chronologically so a viewer can follow while watching the lectures. In the guides all quotes are from Faraday's original lectures. In the endnotes appended to each guide we note any major changes from the original lectures.

A CANDLE:
SOURCES OF ITS FLAME

Key points of the lecture

- Science is a cycle of observation, questioning, and developing theories.

- The wax of the candle is the fuel.

- The heat from the flame melts the wax and the molten wax travels up the wick via capillary action.

- The melted wax is vaporized in order to burn.

- The shape of the flame is due to convection currents.

- An ascending current of air, produced by the heat of the candle, keeps the outside edge cool and forms a cup for the melted wax.

- The formation of a cup at the top of the candle is important in its utility.

- We can think of a large fire as a collection of small, independent flames.

This first lecture begins, as with any scientific investigation, by making observations and asking questions, in this case about the burning of a candle. Inspection shows that the flame does not touch the wax, which is the fuel for the candle. Faraday notes that "when the flame runs down the wick to the wax, it gets extinguished, but it goes on burning in the part above." The wax is a solid substance with "no vessel to contain it," which leads to questions such as:

- How does the solid wax, which will not burn when solid, get to the top of the wick where it does burn?

- When the solid fuel is made a fluid, how does this fluid keep together?

Close observation leads us to see that "a beautiful cup is formed" at the top of the candle, and this cup is filled with molten wax. The heat of the flame melts the wax, but this heat also produces a convection current which forces the surrounding air upward and cools the sides of the wax. This current is produced from the heat of the candle because hot air, being less dense than cold air, rises. The motion of the hot air draws cooler air upward from below the flame.

So, the heat directly melts the wax within the candle and indirectly cools the wax on the outside.

A candle must be able to form this symmetrical cup to be useful; as Faraday notes, the "great beauty in a candle" comes from its utility and that "good looking candles are bad burning ones." For example, non-cylindrical candles, perhaps one shaped like a face or a figurine, burn to form a non-symmetric cup, which, because of an uneven thickness will "gutter." Molten wax will leak through these gutters down the sides of the candle.

We can generalize this insight to all scientific endeavors: "the greatest mistakes and faults with regard to candles, as in many other things" teach us something we otherwise would not have known. Thus, a negative result is as important as a positive result as long as we take the opportunity to learn something from it. That is,

> we come here to be scientists[1] ... [and] whenever a result happens, especially if it be new, you should say, "What is the cause? Why does it occur" and you will in the course of time find out the reason.

This nicely sums up the nature of science and is a theme that permeates all of these lectures.

By examining the action of the heat of the flame, we can learn about the difference between physical and chemical changes. The heat is responsible for "disturbing its [the wax's] proper form if it comes only too near," which undergoes a physical change: it melts the wax to form a fluid. The heat of the flame also causes a chemical change by "destroying the wax itself when it gets hold of it"; that is, the wax, being made fluid and held in the flame, becomes something else entirely by means of combustion. A discussion of the exact nature of this chemical change is delayed until Lectures Two and Three; this lecture focuses on the physical change: how the fluid gets from the cup to the top of the wick where combustion takes place.

As we have already noted, the "flames of burning wicks do not run down to the wax and melt it all away, but keep to their own right place." The heat from the flame at the top of the wick radiates through the air and is conducted through the wick to melt the wax. The melted wax is drawn up the wick to the flame, "very beautifully in the very midst of the center of action which takes place all around it." This is called capillary action.

An everyday event illustrates capillary action: drying our hands with a towel. The water on our hands is drawn into the towel so that "the towel becomes wet with water" just as "the wick becomes wet with wax." A towel thrown over the side of a basin of water and just touching the water draws the water out of the basin like the wick draws the melted wax out of the cup that has formed. This capillary action is what keeps the liquid wax together as it climbs up the wick.

This action can be modelled by filling a hollow glass tube open on both ends with table salt and placing one of the open ends in a dish of ethanol.[2] The dish of ethanol represents the cup of melted wax and the tube of salt represents the wick. The ethanol rises through the salt crystals (the salt does not dissolve in alcohol) until it reaches the top. At the top the ethanol can be lit.

The demonstration implicitly demonstrates that no scientific model is 100 percent accurate. We use models to better understand phenomena, but as with any analogy, there are limits. In this case, for example, our fuel (the ethanol) begins as a liquid not as a solid, as does the wax. This demonstration, then, does not model the melting of the fuel, just the capillary action.

As Faraday noted, solid wax does not burn, nor does melted wax. To burn, the wax must be vaporized. For this reason the flame does not burn to the base of the wick. "The melted wax," he says, "extinguishes the flame." He shows this by turning a burning candle upside down and allowing the wax to drip down out of the wick. In doing so, the flame goes out because it "has not had time to make the fuel hot enough to burn." This demonstration does not, by itself, prove the wax must be vaporized. It could be that the melted wax simply must reach a higher temperature than it is able to when dripping out of the wick. But Faraday shows the "vaporous condition of the fuel" in a fascinating way.

If you blow out a candle carefully, white smoke rises, giving off a distinctive smell. If we are careful we can light this smoke, and the flame will follow the vapor trail back to the wick and relight the wick. But we must do this quickly before the vapor condenses or before the "stream of combustible matter gets disturbed." This shows that the smoke is the vaporous wax, which also explains why the flame must be relit quickly: without flame the vaporized wax begins to cool and solidify. The small particles of solid wax gives the smoke its white color.

Next, the lecture examines the candle's flame. "The flame shines in darkness," Faraday says, "but the light which the diamond has is as nothing until the flame shines upon it…. The candle alone shines by itself, and for itself, or for those who have arranged the materials." Precious metals and jewels may have luster, he says, but theirs is only a reflected glow. The candle's flame is a "bright oblong, brighter at the top than toward the bottom with the wick in the middle…. There is matter rising about it [the flame] which you do not see." This invisible matter will be investigated in Lectures Two through Four, but note here that the characteristic conical shape of a candle flame is caused by rising convection currents which draw the flame upward. The flame is brighter at the top than the bottom because the combustion is incomplete at the bottom ("ignition is not so perfect," Faraday says), of which a fuller discussion is delayed until Lecture Two.

The flame can be studied in more detail by shining a light on the candle and then studying the shadow cast by the flame. The brightest part of the flame gives rise to the darkest part of the shadow, which is discussed in Lecture Two. This method, though, reveals the ascending current of hot air that gives the flame its height, supplies the flame with air, and cools the side of the candle. If the current is disturbed, for example by blowing the air around it, the flame will vary in shape, size, and direction.

Lastly, Faraday turns to a deeper investigation of the flame. A flame changes shape every fraction of a section. To see that he creates a "flame sufficiently large" so it can be thought of as a "multitude of independent candles." The large flame can be thought to show at one time many of the shapes that occur one after another in a candle flame. Faraday mentions a "remarkable breaking out into tongues" due to the "air creeping in over the edge of the dish."[3] The multitude of different shapes of the flame succeed "each other so fast that the eye is only able to take cognizance of them all at once … they seem to us to exist all at one time."

At the end of this lecture we still have many questions that will be answered in lectures that follow.[4] For example, the question "from where does the brightness come?" is answered in Lecture Two. "Where does the candle eventually go?" is covered by Lectures Three and Four. And in Lecture

Five, he explores the relationship between combustion and respiration.

Notes

1. Instead of *scientists* Faraday used *philosophers.* Although today we apply the label *philosopher* only to those practicing philosophy, its earlier definition, according to the *Oxford English Dictionary,* was "a learned person, a scholar." In the nineteenth century, scientists were often called *natural philosophers.*

2. Faraday broke this demonstration into two parts. He used a salt column to demonstrate capillary action. He later placed a piece of rattan cane in a dish of camphine. The camphine rose to the top of the cane, where Faraday ignited it.

3. Faraday demonstrated this by a game familiar to his audience: snapdragon. This popular nineteenth-century parlor game was played in the winter, often on Christmas Eve. A bowl of brandy was heated and then raisins or plums were placed in the brandy, which was ignited. As blue flames rose from the burning brandy, children would pluck the raisins from the burning brandy and eat them—the goal of the game was to not be burned! We substituted a dish filled with cotton balls and ethanol and eliminated any suggestion that children should reach into a burning flame.

4. Because Faraday concluded his lecture with the game of snapdragon, he promised his audience he would spend less time on "these illustrations" and more time "on the philosophy of the thing," i.e., on the science underlying his demonstrations. We chose to replace this with a summary of the lectures to follow in the form of questions.

A CANDLE:
SOURCES OF ITS FLAME

I WILL TELL YOU in five lectures the Chemical History of a Candle. There is *not* a law under which any part of the universe is governed which does not come into play, and is touched upon in the chemistry of a candle. There is no better, there is no more open door by which you can enter into the study of science, than by considering the physical phenomena of a candle. I trust, therefore, I shall not disappoint you in choosing *this* for my subject rather than any newer topic, which could not be better, were it even so good.

So, now, as to the light of the candle. Notice that when the flame runs down the wick to the wax, it gets extinguished, but it goes on burning in the part above. Now, I have no doubt you will ask, how is it that the wax, which will not burn of itself, gets up to the top of the wick, where it will burn? We shall presently examine that; but there is a much more wonderful thing about the burning of a candle than this. You have here a solid substance—the fuel—with no vessel to contain it; and how is it that this can get up to the place where the flame is? How is it that this solid gets there, it not being a fluid? Or, when it is made a fluid, then *how* is it that it keeps together? This is a *wonderful* thing about a candle.

You see that a beautiful cup is formed. As the air comes to the candle it moves upwards by the force of current which the heat of the candle produces, and it so cools all the sides of the wax, as to keep the edge much cooler than the part within; the part within melts by the flame that runs down the wick as far as it can go before it is extinguished, but the part on the outside does *not* melt. The same force of gravity which holds worlds together holds this fluid in a horizontal position, and if the cup be not horizontal, of course the fluid will run away in guttering. You see, therefore, that the cup is formed by this beautifully regular ascending current of air playing upon all sides, which keeps the exterior of the candle cool.

No fuel would serve for a candle which has not the property of giving this cup. These beautiful candles which are irregular and intermittent in their shape cannot have that nicely-formed edge to the cup which is the great beauty in a candle. I hope you will now see that the perfection of a process—that is, its utility—is the better point of beauty about it. It is not the best *looking* thing, but the best *acting* thing, which is the most advantageous to us. These good-looking candles are bad-burning ones. There is guttering because of the irregularity of the stream of air and the badness of the cup which is formed thereby. You may see some pretty examples (and I trust you will notice these instances) of the action of the ascending current when you have a little gutter running down the side of a candle, making it thicker there than it is elsewhere. As the candle goes on burning, that keeps its place and forms a little pillar sticking up by the side, because, as it rises above the rest of the fuel or wax, the air gets better round it, and it is more cooled and better able to resist the action of the heat at a little distance. Now, the great mistakes and faults with regard to candles, as in many other things, often brings with them instruction which we should not receive if they had not occurred. We come here to be scientists; and I hope you will always remember that whenever a result happens, especially if it be new, you should say, "What is the cause? Why does it occur?" and you will in the course of time find out the reason.

Then, there is another point about these candles which will answer a question; that is, as to the way in which this fluid gets out of the cup, up the wick, and into the place of combustion. You see that the flames on these burning wicks do not run down to the wax and melt it all away, but keep to their own right place. They are fenced off from the fluid below, and do not encroach on the cup at the sides. I cannot imagine a more beautiful example than the condition of adjustment under which a candle makes one part subserve to the other to the very end of its action. A combustible thing like that, burning away gradually, never being intruded upon by the flame, is a very beautiful sight; especially when you come to learn what a vigorous thing flame is—what power it has of destroying the wax itself when it gets hold of it, and of disturbing its proper form if it comes only too near.

But how does the flame get hold of the fuel? *Capillary action* conveys the fuel to the part where combustion goes on, and it is deposited there, not in a careless way, but very beautifully in the very midst of the center of action which takes place around it. Now, I am going to give you *two* instances of capillary action. It is that kind of action or attraction which makes two things that do not dissolve in each other still hold together. When you wash your hands, you take a towel to wipe off the water; and it is by that kind of wetting, or that kind of attraction which makes the towel become wet with water, that the wick is made wet with the wax. If you throw the towel over the side of the basin, before long it will draw the water out of the basin like the wick draws the wax out of the candle. Let me show you another application of the same principle.

You see this hollow glass tube filled with table salt. I'll fill the dish with some alcohol colored with red food coloring. You see the fluid rising through the salt. There being no pores in the glass, the fluid cannot go in that direction, but must pass through its length. Already the fluid is at the top of the tube: now I can light it and make it serve as a candle. The fluid has risen by the capillary action of the salt, just as it does through the wick in the candle.

Now, the only reason why the candle does not burn all down the sides of the wick is that the melted wax extinguishes the flame. You know that a candle, if turned upside down, so as to allow the fuel to run upon the wick, will be put out. The reason is that the flame has not had time to make the fuel hot enough to burn, as it does above, where it is carried in small quantities into the wick, and has all the effect of the heat exercised upon it. There is another condition which you must learn as regards the candle, without which you would not be able fully to understand the science of it, and that is the vaporous condition of the fuel. In order that you may understand that, let me show you a very pretty experiment.

If you blow a candle out carefully, you will see the vapor rise from it. You have, I know, often smelled the vapor of a blown-out candle—and a very bad smell it is; but if you blow it out lightly, you will be able to see pretty well the vapor into which this solid matter is transformed. When I hold a lighted match two or three inches from the wick, you can observe a train of fire going through the air till it reaches the candle. I am obliged to be quick and ready, because, if I allow the vapor time to cool, it becomes condensed into a liquid or solid, or the stream of combustible matter gets disturbed.

Now, to the shape or form of the flame. It concerns us much to know about the condition which the matter of the candle finally assumes at the top of the wick—where you have such beauty and brightness as nothing but combustion or flame can produce. You have the glittering beauty of gold and silver, and the still higher luster of jewels, like the ruby and diamond; but none of these rival the brilliancy and beauty of flame. What diamond can shine like flame? It owes its luster at night-time to the very flame shining upon it. The flame shines in darkness, but the light which the diamond has is as nothing until the flame shines upon it, when it is brilliant again. The candle alone shines by itself, and for itself, or for those who have arranged the materials.

The flame is a bright oblong—brighter at the top than toward the bottom—with the wick in the middle, and besides the wick in the middle, certain darker parts toward the bottom, where the ignition is not so perfect as in the part above. Now, let me show you there is a matter rising about it which you do not see.

You can actually see streaming around the flame something which is not part of the flame, but is ascending and drawing the flame upwards. There is a current formed, which draws the flame out—for the flame which you see is really drawn out by the current, and drawn upward to a great height. How remarkable it is that the thing which is light enough to produce shadows of other objects, can be made to throw its own shadow. You observe the shadow of the candle and of the wick; then there is a darkish part and then a part which is more distinct. Curiously enough, however, what we see in the shadow as the darkest part of the flame is, in reality, the brightest part; and here you see streaming upward the ascending current of hot air, which draws out the flame, supplies it with air, and cools the sides of the cup of melted fuel. You know the flame goes up or down; according to the current. You see, then, that we have the power in this way of varying the flame in different directions.

Many of the flames you see here vary in their shape by the currents of air blowing around them in different directions; but we can, if we like, make flames so that they look like fixtures, and we can photograph them—indeed, we have to photograph them, so that they become fixed to us, if we wish to find out everything concerning them.

If I take a flame sufficiently large, it does not keep that homogeneous, that uniform condition of shape, but it breaks out with a power of life which is quite wonderful. In what way does it differ from an ordinary candle? It differs very much in one respect: we have a vivacity and power about it, a beauty and a life entirely different from the light presented by a candle. You see those fine tongues of flame rising up. You have the same general disposition of the mass of the flame from below upwards; but, in addition to that, you have this remarkable breaking out into tongues which you do not perceive in the case of a candle. Now, why is this? You have the air creeping in over the edge of the dish forming these tongues. Why? Because, through the force of the current and the irregularity of the action of the flame, it cannot flow in one uniform stream. The air flows in so irregularly that you have what would otherwise be a single image, broken up into a variety of forms, and each of these little tongues has an independent existence of its own. Indeed, I might say, you have here a multitude of independent candles.

You must not imagine, because you see these tongues all at once, that the flame is of this particular shape. A flame of that shape is never so at any one time. Never is a body of flame, like that which you just saw rising from the ball, of the shape it appears to you. It consists of a multitude of different shapes, succeeding each other so fast that the eye is only able to take cognizance of them all at once. They do not occur all at once: it is only because we see these shapes in such rapid succession, that they seem to us to exist all at one time.

We have thus far spent our time considering the light of the candle, discussing how the fuel gets to the wick and the form of the flame upon combustion. But we have more questions to ponder. From where does the brightness come? And where does the candle eventually go? And in a larger sense, how do the products of combustion lead us to a discussion of the atmosphere? And what is the relationship between combustion and respiration? I started this lecture by claiming that there is no more open door by which to enter into the study of science than by considering the physical phenomena of the candle. Over the next four lectures, I hope to prove this to you.

BRIGHTNESS OF THE FLAME

Key points of the lecture

- The vapor of the wax burns to produce energy given off as light and heat.

- The heat is formed from the reaction between the wax vapor and the air.

- Air is necessary for the combustion of the candle (in Lecture Three we see that it is the oxygen in the air that is necessary).

- The wax must contain carbon. The carbon appears as soot, and sometimes as smoke. Air doesn't contain carbon, so the carbon must have come from the candle.

- Glowing bits of carbon, which are incandescent particles, give the flame its brightness.

- A burning candle produces water and carbon dioxide. Water is investigated further in Lecture Three, and carbon dioxide in Lecture Four.

In this lecture we turn our attention to the brightness of the flame. Faraday notes that we seek "to ascertain what happens in any particular part of the flame—why it happens, what it does in happening, and where, after all, the whole candle goes to." A candle, after all, will burn completely such that it "disappears, if burned properly, without the least trace of dirt in the candlestick."

The lecture starts by examining the darkest part of the flame. By placing one end of a bent glass tube into the middle of the flame and the other end in a flask, we can see a white vapor moving through the tube and filling the flask. It is a vaporous fluid made from the wax that "not only escapes from the end of the tube, but falls down to the bottom of the flask like a heavy substance as indeed it is. We find that it is the wax of the candle made into a vaporous fluid." We call this a vapor, in contrast to a gas: a vapor is "something that will condense" and a gas "remains permanent."

The lecture then explores the properties of this vapor. The nasty smell we perceive from blowing out a candle results from the condensation of this vapor. The lecture demonstrates that the vapor is combustible by melting a large quantity of wax and then igniting its vapor. The heat and light produced by doing this reveal the flammability of the vapor.

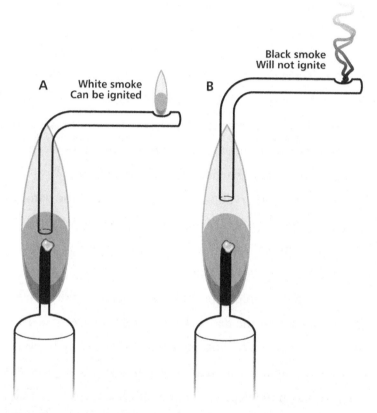

Faraday uses a glass tube with a right-angle bend to probe the flame. **a** *The white smoke produced near the tip of the wick contains vaporized wax and can travel through the pipe and be lit.* **b** *The black smoke produced near the middle of the flame cannot be lit.*

To show where this vapor is produced in the flame we use an "L"-shaped tube to probe different areas of the flame. If we place one end of the tube near the center of the flame, we can then light the vapor that escapes at the other end of the tube. This shows that "in the middle of the flame, where the wick is, there is this combustible vapor" because the vapor coming from this part of the flame will ignite.

Next, we raise the glass tube to the upper part of the flame. The vapor that is released can no longer combust because it has already burned. This shows us that "there are clearly two different kinds of action—one the production of the vapor, and the other the combustion of it—both of which take place in particular parts of the candle."

These two observations hint at the cause of the flame's spatial heterogeneity: the flame's varying colors, brightness, and temperatures arise because of distinct actions occurring in different parts of the flame.

By some simple experiments we can explore these different parts of the flame. For example, we can visualize the temperature distribution within the flame by holding a piece of paper in the flame for a few seconds. A black ring forms on the paper, its center almost untouched. This shows that the inner part of the flame is not hot enough to burn the paper, but the outer edge of the flame, where the vaporous wax and the oxygen meet, burns the paper. There is a ring "because the heat is where the air and the fuel come together" resulting in "intense chemical action."

This observation shows that "air is absolutely necessary for combustion." This necessity is further demonstrated by placing a jar over a lit candle. At first the candle burns normally, but then the flame fades, flickers, and goes out. This happens because the air trapped in the jar changes. As scientists we want to investigate this new insight: why is a candle put out "by the want of air?"

To explore incomplete combustion we create a large "wick" from a pile of cotton balls. As it burns we see a "black substance going up into the atmosphere." This black substance is soot and we do not see it when a candle burns, although, if we look at the underside of the paper we used to produce the ring, we see it is covered in soot. Why do we not see this soot when the candle burns "in a pure and proper state of air?" That is, the candle obviously produces soot (charcoal or carbon) as seen on the paper. But we do not see this soot escape the flame of a candle as we did with the cotton balls.

Later in this lecture Faraday shows that the soot is consumed by the flame in a well-burning candle. Next, though, he shows that carbon particles glow in the flame before being consumed.

We will use a mixture of gunpowder and iron filings to examine combustion and incandescence. This will help us to better understand the nature of the different types of light we see in the flame. Gunpowder "contains carbon and other materials which altogether cause it to burn with a flame."[1] We place in this gunpowder iron filings, that is, small pieces of pulverized iron. When we burn this mixture in the air, the gunpowder sets fire to the filings and we can see "the difference between substances burning with flame and not with flame." Faraday says this combustion is of "two kinds," although today we would talk of combustion and incandescence. The gunpowder burns with a flame but the iron filings remain solid and thus do not produce a flame but glow instead. "Upon these differences depends all the utility and all the beauty of flame which we use for the purpose of giving off light." As we shall see, these "two kinds" occur within a candle flame as well.

To demonstrate further these "two kinds" we use lycopodium powder, which is very combustible and consists of separate little particles. When it burns it produces a "cloud of flame" accompanied by a "rushing noise." Each particle produces vapor and thus its own flame, yet when it burns in bulk it appears as one giant flame. This is not, though, an example of combustion like that of the iron filings because the lycopodium particles are vaporized, while the iron filings remain solid.

We can see these two ways to produce light—Faraday calls them "two types of combustion"—in a candle by inserting again the "L"-shaped tube in the flame (see previous figure). If we place an end in the brightest part of the flame, black smoke issues from the other end. This smoke cannot be ignited, no matter how hard we try. The smoke contains carbon which must exist in the candle's wax before being released into the flame. Because this carbon consists of solid particles (like the iron filings), we see a bright light. That is, "whenever a substance burns, as the iron filings burned in the flame of the gunpowder, without assuming the vaporous state ... it becomes exceedingly luminous ... it is to this presence of solid particles in the candle flame that it owes its brilliancy." We say that the carbon particles undergo incandescence, or simply that they glow. As Faraday notes "the flame of the candle owes its brightness to the separation, during combustion, of these particles of carbon."

This incandescence also occurs when we place a piece of charcoal in a flame, which glows like the particles of carbon that are "set free" from the vapor of the wax. Burning charcoal yields a black smoke, rarely seen in a burning candle because the "particles when burned never pass off from a candle in the form of carbon. They go off into the air as a perfectly invisible substance." That substance, although not named here, is carbon dioxide, which is thoroughly discussed in Lecture Four. The main point here is that the carbon that comes from the candle incandesces (glows) to form the brightest part of the flame, and then reacts with oxygen to create the hottest part of the flame.

Faraday emulates the "intense chemical reaction" at the edge of the flame by adding a drop of sulfuric acid to a mixture of potassium chlorate and sugar.[2] The potassium chlorate reacts, it oxidizes the carbon in the sugar to form carbon dioxide and water. It also produces the carbon particles that we can see glowing. This illustrates that "all things that burn and produce solid particles," such as a candle, iron filings, and the potassium chlorate and sugar. He calls the emission from these processes "glorious and beautiful light."

To demonstrate the effect of oxygen on combustion we use a Bunsen burner.[3] This device lets us adjust the amount of oxygen mixed with the fuel, in this case propane gas. Propane has the chemical formula C_3H_8, and so, like candle wax, it is a hydrocarbon. When only a small amount of air is mixed with the propane it burns with a bright yellow flame. The color arises from incomplete combustion, which means that there isn't enough oxygen to burn all the carbon in the propane so small particles of unburned carbon are released. When we adjust the burner so that more air, and thus more oxygen, is mixed with the propane, the flame becomes pale and blue. This oxygen-enriched fuel reacts with all the carbon in the propane so there are no particles to be set free.

In this lecture, then, we see that carbon is a product of combustion, appearing as soot. We have also discussed that the carbon, upon being released from the flame, burns again to produce other products. Faraday shows this by covering a burning candle with a vessel. The sides of the vessel become opaque and cloudy and the

> light begins to burn feebly. It is the products, you see, which make the light so dim, and this is the same thing which makes the sides of the vessel so opaque.

To see what material clouds the walls we take a cold spoon and hold it over a candle, being care to not "soot" the spoon. The spoon becomes dim: water condenses on the spoon from the candle's emissions. We will discuss the water created by the candle in Lecture Three.

Notes

1. Gunpowder is a mixture of carbon, sulfur, and potassium nitrate.
2. Instead of potassium chlorate and sugar, Faraday used antimony trisulfide as the oxidant. Antimony trisulfide was used in the manufacture of safety matches, ammunition, explosives and fireworks.
3. Instead of a Bunsen burner, Faraday used an *air-burner*. A footnote in the original lecture explains this device: "It consists of a cylindrical metal chimney, covered at the top with a piece of rather coarse iron-wire gauze. This is supported over an Argand burner, in such a manner that the gas may mix in the chimney with an amount of air sufficient to burn the carbon and hydrogen simultaneously, so that there may be no separation of carbon in the flame with consequent deposition of soot. The flame, being unable to pass through the wire gauze, burns in a steady, nearly invisible manner above."

LECTURE TWO

BRIGHTNESS OF THE FLAME

WE WERE OCCUPIED the last time we met in considering the general character and arrangement as regards the fluid portion of a candle, and the way in which that fluid got into the place of combustion. And now, I have to ask your attention to the means by which we are enabled to ascertain what happens in any particular part of the flame—why it happens, what it does in happening, and where, after all, the whole candle goes to, because, as you know very well, a candle being brought before us and burned, disappears, if burned properly, without the least trace of dirt in the candlestick—and this is a very curious phenomenon. We will examine this dark part first.

And now, I take this bent glass tube, and introduce one end into the middle of the flame. You see at once that something is coming from the flame. At the other end you will see that something from the middle part of the flame is gradually drawn out, and goes through the tube and into that flask, and there behaves very differently from what it does in the open air. It not only escapes from the end of the tube, but falls down to the bottom of the flask like a heavy substance, as indeed it is. We find that it is the wax of the candle made into a vaporous fluid—not a gas. (You must learn the difference between a gas and a vapor: a gas remains permanent, a vapor is something that will condense.) If you blow out a candle, you perceive a very nasty smell, resulting from the condensation of this vapor. This is very different from what you have outside the flame; and, in order to make that more clear to you, I am about to produce and set fire to a larger portion of this vapor—for what we have in the small way in a candle, to understand thoroughly, we must, as scientists, produce in a larger way, if needful, that we may examine the different parts.

Here is some wax in a glass flask, and I've made it hot, as the inside of that candle-flame is hot, and the matter about the wick is hot. You see that the wax has become fluid, and there is a little smoke coming from it and vapor rising up that I can set on fire. This, then, is exactly the same kind of vapor as we have in the middle of the candle.

I have arranged another tube carefully in the flame, and I was able, by a little care, to get that vapor to pass through the tube to the other extremity, where I will light it, and obtain absolutely the flame of the candle at a place distant from it. Now, look at that. Is not that a very pretty experiment? And you see from this that there are clearly two different kinds of action—one the production of the vapor, and the other the combustion of it—both of which take place in particular parts of the candle.

I shall get no vapor from that part which is already burnt. If I raise the tube to the upper part of the flame, so soon as the vapor has been swept away, what comes away will be no longer combustible: it is already burned. How burned? Why, burned thus: in the middle of the flame, where the wick is, there is this combustible vapor; on the outside of the flame is the air which we shall find necessary for the burning of the candle; between the two, intense chemical action takes place, whereby the air and the fuel act upon each other, and at the very same time that we obtain light the vapor itself is consumed. If you examine where the heat of a candle is, you will find it very curiously arranged. Suppose I take this candle, and hold a piece of paper close upon the flame, where is the heat of that flame?

Do you not see that it is not in the inside? It is in a ring, exactly in the place where I told you the chemical action was; and even in my irregular mode of making this experiment, if there is not too much disturbance, there will always be a ring because the heat is where the air and the fuel come together.

This is most important for us as we proceed with our subject. Air is absolutely necessary for combustion; and, what is more, I must have you understand that *fresh* air is necessary, or else we should be imperfect in our reasoning and our experiments.

Here is a jar of air. I place it over a candle, and it burns very nicely in it at first, showing that what I have said about it is true; but there will soon be a change. See how the flame is drawing upwards, presently fading, and at last going out. And going out, why? The jar is full of air, partly changed, partly not changed; but it does not contain sufficient of the fresh air which is necessary for the combustion of a candle. These are all points which we, as young chemists, have to gather up; and if we look a little more closely into this kind of action, we shall soon find certain steps of reasoning extremely interesting. We have the case of the combustion of a candle; we have the case of a candle being put out by the want of air; and we have now the case of imperfect combustion; and this is to us so interesting, that I want you to understand it as thoroughly as you do the case of a candle burning in its best possible manner. I will now make a great flame, because we need the largest possible illustration.

Here is a larger wick made from these cotton balls. All these things are the same as candles, after all. If we have larger wicks, we must have a larger supply of air, or we shall have less perfect combustion. Now look at the black substance going up into the atmosphere; there is a regular stream of it. Look at the soot that flies off from the flame: see what an imperfect combustion it is, because it cannot get enough air. What, then, is happening? Why, certain things which are necessary to the combustion of a candle are absent, and very bad results are accordingly produced; but we see what happens to a candle when it is burnt in a pure and proper state of air. Recall the charred ring on the paper, and on the other side you see that the burning of a candle produces the same kind of soot—charcoal or carbon.

Let me explain to you—as it is quite necessary for our purpose—that, although I take a candle and give you, as the general result, its combustion in the form of a flame, we must see whether combustion is always in this condition, or whether there are other conditions of flame; and we shall soon discover that there are, and that they are most important to us.

Here is a little gunpowder. You know that gunpowder burns with flame—we may fairly call it flame. It contains carbon and other materials, which altogether cause it to burn with a flame. And here is some pulverised iron, or iron filings. Now, I propose burning these two things together. My object being to make the gunpowder set fire to the filings and burn them in the air, and thereby show the difference between substances burning with flame and not with flame. Now, here is the mixture; and when I set fire to it, you must watch the combustion, and you will see that it is of two kinds. You will see the gunpowder burning with a flame, and the filings thrown up. You will see them burning too, but without the production of flame. They will each burn separately. There is the gunpowder, which burns with a flame; and there are the filings—they burn with a different kind of combustion. You see, then, these two great distinctions; and upon these differences depend all the utility and all the beauty of flame which we use for the purpose of giving off light. When we use oil, or gas, or candle, for the purpose of illumination, their fitness all depends upon these different kinds of combustion.

There are such curious conditions of flame, that it requires some cleverness and nicety of discrimination to distinguish the kinds of combustion one from another. For instance, here is a powder which is very combustible, consisting, as you see, of separate little particles. It is called lycopodium, and each of these particles can produce a vapor, and produce its own flame; but, to see them burning, you would imagine it was all one flame. I will now set fire to a quantity, and you will see the effect. We saw a cloud of flame, apparently in one body; but that rushing noise was proof that the combustion was not a continuous or a regular one. This is not an example of combustion like that of the filings I have been speaking of, to which we must now return.

Suppose I take a candle, and examine that part of it which appears brightest to our eyes. Why? There I get those black particles, which already you have seen many times evolved from the flame, and which I am now about to evolve in a different way. I have arranged the glass tube so as just to dip into this luminous part, as in our first experiment, only higher. You see the result. In place of having the same white vapor that we had before, we now have a black vapor. There it goes, as black as ink. It is certainly very different from the white vapor; and when we put a light to it, we shall find that it does not burn. Well, these particles, as I said before, are just the smoke of the candle. Why, it is the same carbon which exists in the candle. And how comes it out of the candle wax? It evidently existed in the wax, or else we should not have had it here. And now I want you to follow me in this explanation. You would hardly think that all those substances which flew around London, in the form of soots and blacks, are the very beauty and life of the flame, and which are burned as those iron filings were burned.

I want you now to follow me in this point, that whenever a substance burns, as the iron filings burnt in the flame of gunpowder, without assuming the vaporous state (whether it becomes liquid or remains solid), it becomes exceedingly luminous. What I have to say is applicable to all substances, whether they burn or whether they do not burn; that they are exceedingly bright if they retain their solid form, and that it is to this presence of solid particles in the candle-flame that it owes its brilliancy.

I have here a piece of carbon or charcoal, which will burn and give us light exactly in the same manner as if it were burnt as part of a candle. The heat that is in the flame of a candle decomposes the vapor of the wax, and sets free the carbon particles—they rise up heated and glowing as this now glows, and then enter into the air. But the particles when burnt never pass off from a candle in the form of carbon. They go off into the air as a perfectly invisible substance. I shall tell you about this later.

Is it not beautiful to think that such a process is going on, and that such a dirty thing as charcoal can become so incandescent? You see it comes to this—that all bright flames contain these solid particles; all things that burn and produce solid particles, either during the time they are burning, as in the candle, or immediately after being burnt, as in the case of the gunpowder and iron-filings—all these things give us this glorious and beautiful light.

I've mixed potassium chlorate and sugar. I shall touch them with a drop of sulfuric acid, for the purpose of giving you an illustration of chemical action, and they will instantly burn. Now, from the appearance of things, you can judge for yourselves whether they produce solid matter in burning. I have given you the train of reasoning which will enable you to say whether they do or do not; for what is this bright flame but the solid particles passing off?

When the particles are not separated, you get no brightness. The flame of a candle owes its brightness to the separation, during combustion, of these particles of carbon. I can very quickly alter that arrangement.

Here, for instance, is a bright yellow flame from propane in a Bunsen burner. Supposing I add so much air to the flame as to cause all to burn before those particles are set free, I shall not have this brightness. There is plenty of carbon in the gas; but, because the atmosphere can get to it, and mix with it before it burns, you see how pale and blue the flame is. The difference is solely due to the solid particles not being separated before the gas is burnt.

You observe that there are certain products as the result of the combustion of a candle, and that of these products one portion may be considered as charcoal, or soot; that charcoal, when afterwards burnt, produces some other product; and it concerns us very much now to ascertain what that other product is.

This vessel captures all the products of the candle, and you will presently see that the vessel's walls become quite opaque. The sides of the jar become cloudy, and the light begins to burn feebly. It is the products, you see, which make the light so dim, and this is the same thing which makes the sides of the vessel so opaque.

If I take a spoon that has been in the cold water, wipe it dry, and hold it over a candle—so as not to soot it—you will find that it becomes dim, just as the vessel's walls are dim.

And now, just to carry your thoughts forward to the time we shall next meet, let me tell you that it is water which causes the dimness. I will show you that we can make it, without difficulty, assume the form of a liquid.

PRODUCTS OF COMBUSTION

Key points of the lecture

- Water, as shown at the end of Lecture Two, is one of the products from a burning candle.

- Electrolysis shows that hydrogen and oxygen comprise water.

- Oxygen comes from the air suggesting it does not exist in significant amounts in the candle wax.

- Hydrogen must be in the candle because it is not in the air.

- Hydrogen gas is reactive and is less dense than air.

- Air is not pure oxygen (this will be further examined in Lecture Four).

The previous lecture concluded with experiments that isolated the products of a burning candle. Carbon appeared as either incandescent particles, which gave the flame its brightness, or as black smoke. Water condensed on a cold spoon held above the candle's flame. And a badly burning candle produced black smoke that contained a "perfectly invisible substance." That substance, unnamed in the lecture, was carbon dioxide, which will be investigated in Lecture Four. This lecture examines, in more detail, water and its constituent elements hydrogen and oxygen.

We collect water by placing a lit candle under an ice-filled glass container. As the water vapor issuing from the candle strikes the outer surface of the container, it condenses, and appears as drops of liquid. Although not demonstrated in the lecture, we could do this experiment in dry air—air free of water vapor—and see the same result.

Next, the lecture demonstrates that the liquid gathered on the container's surface is water. We test it by seeing if it reacts with potassium. First, we do a control experiment by dropping potassium metal into a substance we know is water. We see, says Faraday, the metal "lighting up and floating about, burning with a violent flame." Next, we test the liquid gathered from the candle: it too reacts with potassium. This shows us that this liquid is chemically similar to water, and provides evidence that it is, in fact, water. Note, too, that hydrogen gas is a product of the reaction with potassium and water. The reactivity of hydrogen is discussed later in this lecture, but note here that as the hydrogen is released from the water it produces heat, burning with a violet flame.

Faraday then makes a point fundamental to the lectures: the idea that a scientific explanation unifies the physical world that surrounds us. "Water," says Faraday, "as water, remains always the same, either in solid, liquid, or fluid state ... [and is] absolutely the same thing whether it is produced from a candle, by combustion, or from the rivers or oceans.... Water is a thing compounded of two substances, one of which we have derived from the candle and the other we shall find elsewhere." Faraday is alluding to hydrogen and oxygen, both of which we'll investigate later in the lecture.

The lecture next explores that idea that while water is "the same thing," it comes in different forms with different physical properties. Water may occur as a solid, called ice, or as a vapor called steam. Liquid water is water "in its densest state." That is, if we cool it to ice or heat it to steam, the volume of the water increases. The lecture demonstrates the effect of heat by adding a small amount of liquid water to a metal bottle, and then heating it to turn the liquid into steam. The steam fills that bottle and issues from it. A watch glass held over the bottle will condense the exiting steam.

The lecture then vividly demonstrates the volume change when steam turns into a liquid. We turn off the heat and quickly seal the bottle to trap the steam inside, and then plunge it into a cold water bath. The bottle dramatically collapses as the steam turn to liquid, "there being," Faraday notes, "a vacuum produced inside by the condensation of the steam."

These experiments demonstrate that when we add heat to liquid water or cool steam, we still have water; that it has not changed into "other things." Chemically it is still the same, only changed physically: a cubic inch of water, for example, will expand to about a cubic foot of steam when we heat it, and then contract again when cooled.

While water increases in volume from liquid to vapor "largely and wonderfully," it also increases in volume from liquid to solid "very strangely and powerfully." The lecture demonstrates the volume change that occurs when liquid water become a solid. Faraday seals water as a liquid in a cast iron vessel and then drops it into a mixture of dry ice and acetone.[1] This -78°C cold bath causes the water inside the iron vessel to freeze. The water expands and shatters the iron vessel, even though the vessel's wall is about a third of an inch in thickness. This volume increase when water turns to ice—a change opposite to most other substances—shows again how science unifies our understanding of the physical world: water floats on ice because "the ice is larger than the quantity of water which can produce it."

So, any changes in the physical state of water still give

us water, the same substance from a burning candle or the ocean. But how do we get water from a candle? We saw earlier that there must be carbon in the candle, and we may be confident that something that makes up water must be part of the candle as well. Water "is not in the candle; and it is not in the air round about the candle which is necessary for its combustion. It is neither in one nor the other, but it comes from their combined action [a chemical reaction], a part from the candle, a part from the air."[2]

To understand the composition of water we use electricity "to pull the water to pieces." The electricity adds energy to the water "as though [we] were applying heat to cause the water to appear to boil." This results in two gases that we gather in burets. Our first observation is that we get twice as much of one gas, as measured by volume, as of the other. Although not made explicit in the lecture this reflects the chemical formula of water, H_2O. This implies that we get two hydrogen atoms and one oxygen atom for each molecule of water pulled to "pieces"; this shows up as the 2:1 ratio we see in the volumes of the gases.[3] Neither of these gases condense and so we know that they are not steam. Steam, recall, is a vapor, and a vapor can be condensed.

We examine the gas of greater volume first. When a small amount is held in a flame it ignites with a "pop"— further evidence that this is not steam since steam will put out a fire. Faraday demonstrates that this gas is less dense than air by allowing it to displace air: he turns a bottle filled with air upside down and places it on top of a bottle filled with the unnamed gas. To determine that the gas in the bottom bottle has replaced the air, Faraday ignites the gas in the upper bottle. This gas is hydrogen and it is contained in the candle wax, a mixture of molecules consisting of carbon and hydrogen, and called collectively "hydrocarbons."

Hydrogen is an element because we can get nothing else from it, like we can get hydrogen from the water or carbon from the candle. Thus a candle is not an element either, although carbon is an element. Hydrogen gets its name from the Greek words for "water generator."

We can see that hydrogen gas has a lower density than air by using it to form soap bubbles. Bubbles filled with our breath, which is mixture of air and carbon dioxide, fall; bubbles filled with hydrogen gas rapidly ascend. As Faraday notes, we see "how light this gas must be in order to carry with it not merely the ordinary soap-bubble, but the larger portion of a drop hanging to the bottom." Hydrogen gas was formerly used in airships, most famously the *Hindenburg,* in which hydrogen's density and reactivity were both on display.[4]

Next the lecture turns to the other gas formed by the electrolysis of water: oxygen. When water is formed from the burning candle, the hydrogen in the candle combines with the oxygen in the air surrounding the flame. To see that there is oxygen in the air we compare a candle burning in air with one burning in pure oxygen. Both support combustion, but the candle burns more brightly in pure oxygen. In Lecture Four we will learn how important it is that air is not pure oxygen: our world would burn away if this were so. Faraday notes that oxygen does not just support "the combustion of hydrogen, or carbon, or of the candle; but it exalts all combustion of the common kind."

To demonstrate this we show the effect of oxygen on the combustion of hydrogen. When hydrogen and oxygen are "mixed in the same proportion in which they occur in water"—that is, two volumes of hydrogen with one volume of oxygen—and used to fill soap bubbles we see a flame and hear a loud noise. The hydrogen and oxygen gases react with each other to produce water and a great deal of energy.

We then return to the first demonstration in this lecture to now ask "why does a piece of potassium decompose water?" The reason is because there is oxygen in the water. The hydrogen in the water is set free as a gas and it is the hydrogen that then burns in the air. Faraday shows the same reaction by placing a piece of potassium on ice, which illustrates his point from earlier in the lecture that "water remains always the same, either in solid, liquid, or fluid state."

In the next lecture Faraday explores why we can burn a candle, or gas in our homes, or fuel in our fireplaces without these "strange and injurious actions" that we saw when reacting potassium and water, hydrogen and oxygen, and burning a candle in pure oxygen.

Notes

1. Faraday used a "mixture of salt and pounded ice." A footnote in the original lecture explains: "A mixture of salt and pounded ice reduces the temperature from 32°F to zero—the ice at the same time becoming fluid."

2. Faraday's statement means that the hydrogen comes from the candle and the oxygen from the air. Air can be humid, i.e., contain water, but this is not the source of water from a burning candle because if a candle is burned in dry air it produces water.

3. What is actually produced is *diatomic* hydrogen and oxygen in a 2:1 ratio: $2H_2O(l) \rightarrow 2H_2(g) + O_2(g)$.

4. The *Hindenburg* was built long after Faraday's death. In the original lecture he referred to hydrogen-filled balloons.

LECTURE THREE

PRODUCTS OF COMBUSTION

WHEN WE PARTED WE had just mentioned the word "products" from the candle. For when a candle burns we found we were able to get various products from it. There was one substance which was not obtained when the candle was burning properly, which was charcoal or smoke; and there was some other substance that went upwards from the flame which did not appear as smoke, but took some other form, and made part of that general current which, ascending from the candle upwards, becomes invisible, and escapes. There were also other products to mention. You remember that in that rising current having its origin at the candle, we found that one part was condensable against a cold spoon and another part was incondensable.

We will first take the condensable part, and examine it;

and, strange to say, we find that that part of the product is just water—nothing but water. On the last occasion I spoke of it incidentally, merely saying that water was produced among the condensable products of the candle; but today I wish to draw your attention to water, that we may examine it carefully, especially in relation to this subject, and also with respect to its general existence on the surface of the globe.

Now, having previously arranged an experiment for the purpose of condensing water from the products of the candle, my next point will be to show you this water; and perhaps one of the best means that I can adopt for showing its presence is to exhibit a very visible action of water, and then to apply that test to what is collected as a drop at the bottom of the vessel. A small piece of potassium shows the presence of water by lighting up and floating about, burning with a violent flame. You see a drop of water—a condensed product of the candle—hanging from under the surface of the dish. I will show you that the potassium has the same action upon it as upon the water in the dish in the experiment we have just tried. I will take a drop upon a glass slide, and when I put the potassium to it, you will see at once, from it taking fire, that there is water present.

Now, that water was produced by the candle. Water is one individual thing—it never changes. We can add to it by careful adjustment, for a little while, or we can take it apart, and get other things from it; but water, as water, remains always the same, either in a solid, liquid, or fluid state.

And now—to go into the history of this wonderful production of water from combustibles, and by combustion—I must first of all tell you that this water may exist in different conditions; and although you may now be acquainted with all its forms, they still require us to give a little attention to them for the present, so that we may perceive how the water, while it goes through its protean changes, is entirely and absolutely the same thing, whether it is produced from a candle, by combustion, or from the rivers or ocean.

First of all, water, when at the coldest, is ice. Now, we scientists speak of water as water, whether it be in its liquid, or solid, or gaseous state—we speak of it chemically as water. Water is a thing compounded of two substances, one of which we have derived from the candle, and the other which we shall find elsewhere. Water may occur as ice. Ice changes back into water when the temperature is raised: water also changes into steam when it is warmed enough. The water which I have before me is in its densest state, and although it changes in condition, in form, and in many other qualities, it still is water; and whether we change it into steam by heat, or whether we alter it into ice by cooling, it increases in volume—in the first case very largely and wonderfully, and in the second very strangely and powerfully.

For instance, I will have this metal bottle, into which I've poured a little water. I'm converting the water into steam, for the purpose of showing to you the different volumes which water occupies in its different states of liquid water and water vapor or steam. See what a stream of vapor is issuing from this bottle! You observe that we must have made it quite full of steam to have it sent out in that great quantity. And now, as we can convert the water into steam by heat, we convert it back into liquid water by the application of cold. And if we take a watch glass and hold it over this steam, see how soon it gets damp with water; it will condense until the glass is warm—it condenses the water which is now running down the sides of it.

I have here another experiment to show the condensation of water from a vaporous state back into a liquid state, in the same way as the vapor, one of the products of the candle, was condensed against the bottom of the dish, and obtained in the form of water; and to show you how truly and thoroughly these changes take place, I will take this bottle, which is now full of steam, and close the top. We shall see what takes place when we cause this water or steam to return back to the fluid state by cooling it in water. You see what has happened. If I had closed the lid, and still kept the heat applied to it, it would have burst the vessel; yet, when the steam returns to the state of liquid water, the bottle collapses, there being a vacuum produced inside by the condensation of the steam.

I show you these experiments for the purpose of pointing out that in all these occurrences there is nothing that changes the water into any other thing—it still remains water; and so the vessel is obliged to give way, and is crushed inwards, as in the other case, by the further application of heat, it would have been blown outwards.

And what do you think the bulk of that water is when it assumes the vaporous condition? A cubic inch of water will expand to a cubic foot of steam; and, on the contrary, the application of cold will contract that large amount of steam into this small quantity of water.

Let us now take the case of water changing into ice: we can effect that by cooling the water in a dry ice/acetone bath; and I shall do so to show you that when water becomes ice, it changes in volume in an extraordinary way. These bottles are made of cast iron; they are very strong and very thick—I suppose they are each a third of an inch in thickness. I've filled this one with water, to exclude all air, and I'll screw the plug in tightly. We shall see that when we freeze the water in the vessel, it will not be able to hold the ice, and the expansion within will break it into pieces. No communication will take place, you observe, between the water in the bottle and the ice in the outer bowl. But there will be a conveyance of heat from one to the other. The cold has taken possession of the bottle and its contents.

Although the iron was thick, the ice has burst it asunder. You see some ice, partly enclosed by the covering of iron which is too small for them, because the ice is larger in bulk than the water. You know very well that ice floats on water. Why? Because the ice is larger than the quantity of water which can produce it; and therefore the ice weighs the lighter, and the water is the heavier.

To return to our quiet philosophy. We shall not in future be deceived, therefore, by any changes that are produced in water. Water is the same everywhere, whether produced from the ocean or from the flame of the candle. Where, then, is the water which we get from a candle? I must anticipate a little, and tell you. It evidently comes, as to part of it, from the candle; but is it within the candle beforehand? No. It is not in the candle; and it is not in the air round about the candle which is necessary for its combustion. It is neither in one nor the other, but it comes from their combined action, a part from the candle, a part from the air; and this we have now to trace, so that we may understand thoroughly what is the chemical history of a candle when we have it burning on our table.

How shall we get at this? I myself know plenty of ways, but I want you to get at it from the association in your minds of what I have already told you. I think you can see a little in this way. I'll use electricity to pull water to pieces. This power supply makes it as though I were applying heat to cause the water to appear to boil. When we separate or electrolyze water into its parts we get two volumes of one gas, and one of another. The gases produced are not steam. Steam is condensible into water, and when you lower the temperature of steam, you convert it back into fluid water. As you know water is liquid at room temperature. Notice that this gas, which I have collected, does not become a liquid. I will take another test and apply it to this gas. If I now apply a light to the mouth of the test tube, it ignites with a slight noise. That tells you that it is not steam. Steam puts out a fire—it does not burn; but you saw that what I had in this test tube burnt. We may obtain this substance equally from water produced from the candle-flame as from any other source.

Here is a vial full of the same gas. I will show you something most interesting. It is a combustible gas; but it is also less dense than air. Steam will condense: this body will rise in the air, and not condense.

Suppose I take another vial, empty of all but air: if I examine it with a flame, I shall find that it contains nothing but air. I will now take this vial full of the gas that I am speaking of, and deal with it as though it were a light body. I will hold both upside-down, and turn the one up under the other. And now what does the vial contain that had the gas procured from the steam? You will find it only contains air. But look! Here is the combustible substance which I have poured out of the one vial into the other. It still preserves its quality, and condition, and independence, and therefore is the more worthy of our consideration, as belonging to the products of a candle. This is what we get from water—the same substance which is contained in the candle.

Let us now trace distinctly the connection between these two points. This is hydrogen—a body classed among those things which in chemistry we call elements, because we can get nothing else out of them. A candle is *not* an elementary body, because we can get carbon out of it; we can get this hydrogen out of it, or at least out of the water which it supplies. And this gas has been so named hydrogen, because it is that element which, in association with another element, generates water.

This hydrogen is a very beautiful substance. It is so light that it carries things up: it is far lighter than the atmosphere; and I dare say I can show you this by an experiment.

Here is our tank of hydrogen, and here are some soapsuds. I have a rubber tube connected with the hydrogen tank, and at the end of it is a plastic pipe. Now, I could blow bubbles with my breath, or, blow bubbles by means of the hydrogen. You observe how the bubbles fell downwards when I blew them with my warm breath; but notice the difference when I blow them with hydrogen. It shows you how light this gas must be in order to carry with it not merely the ordinary soap-bubble, but the larger portion of a drop hanging to the bottom of it. I can show its lightness in a better way than this: larger bubbles than these may be so lifted up—indeed, in former times balloons used to be filled with this gas.

Water also contains oxygen. Oxygen, as you will immediately imagine, exists in the atmosphere; for how should the candle burn to produce water without it? Such a thing would be absolutely impossible, and chemically impossible, without oxygen. Now, as regards this very property of oxygen supporting combustion, which we may compare to air, I will take a piece of candle to show it to you in a rough way, and the result will be rough. You see the combustion in air. How will it burn in oxygen? I have here a jar of oxygen for you to compare the action of this gas with that of air. See how brightly and how beautifully it burns! Is it wonderful how great the supporting powers of oxygen are as regards combustion? But it does not affect merely the combustion of hydrogen, or carbon, or the candle; but it exalts all combustions of the common kind. We must now, for a little while longer, look at it with respect to hydrogen.

I am now about to set fire to oxygen and hydrogen, mixed in the proportion in which they occur in water. Here is a vessel of soap bubbles made with one volume of oxygen and two volumes of hydrogen exactly of the same nature as the gas we obtained from electrolysis. I will take a bubble in my hand and you will perhaps think I am acting oddly in this experiment; but it is to show you that we must not always trust to noise and sound, but rather to real facts. This oxygen united with the hydrogen, as you saw by the phenomena, and heard by the sound, with the utmost readiness of action, and all its powers were taken up in its neutralization of the qualities of the hydrogen.

So now I think you will perceive the whole history of water with reference to oxygen and the air, from what we have said before.

Why does a piece of potassium decompose water? Because it finds oxygen in the water. What is set free when I put it in the water? It sets free hydrogen, and the hydrogen burns; but the potassium itself combines with oxygen; and this piece of potassium, in taking the water apart—the water, you may say, derived from the combustion of the candle—takes away the oxygen which the candle took from the air, and so sets the hydrogen free; and even if I take a piece of ice, and put a piece of potassium upon it, the beautiful affinities by which the oxygen and the hydrogen are related are such, that the ice will absolutely set fire to the potassium. It produces a sort of volcanic action.

It will be my place, when next we meet, having pointed out these anomalous actions, to show you that none of these extra and strange effects are met with by us—that none of these strange and injurious actions take place when we are burning, not merely a candle, but gas in our homes, or fuel in our fireplaces, so long as we confine ourselves within the laws that Nature has made for our guidance.

THE NATURE OF THE ATMOSPHERE

Key points of the lecture

- Air contains oxygen and nitrogen gases; it is about 80 percent nitrogen and 20 percent oxygen by volume.

- Oxygen gas sustains burning; nitrogen gas is nonreactive (inert) and its presence is merely to give pressure to the atmosphere.

- Gases are compressible.

- Gases have mass and we can measure the mass; a specific volume of different gases have different masses even at the same conditions of pressure and temperature and we can determine these masses.

- Carbon dioxide, like nitrogen, does not sustain

burning, in contrast to oxygen.

- Carbon dioxide gas appears as a product from the reaction of an acid with marble, chalk, shells, and corals.

- Carbon dioxide has a greater density than air.

- Carbon dioxide will be further considered in Lecture Five, including its composition and its role in respiration.

In the previous lecture Faraday shows that a candle produces water by combining hydrogen in the candle's wax with oxygen from the air. We also observed that a candle burns better in pure oxygen than air. This leads us to a question: "How is it that the air and the oxygen do not equally well burn the candle?" The answer, Faraday notes, "relates most intimately to the nature of the atmosphere, and it is most important to us."

To investigate this question Faraday studies the difference between air and oxygen using a chemical reaction. In the "blue bottle experiment" we mix oxygen and a solution of potassium hydroxide, glucose, and methylene blue in a sealed flask.[1] When we shake the mixture the solution turns dark blue. When we substitute air for oxygen we see again the blue color, which shows that oxygen is in the air. And then we notice a difference: the blue color fades in both flasks, but it does so more quickly in the flask with air than in the flask with pure oxygen. This shows that air is not pure oxygen; that is

> there is in air, besides oxygen, something else present. This
> solution left something untouched—there is, in fact, a gas
> in air, which the solution cannot touch, and this gas is not
> oxygen, and yet is part of the atmosphere.

This "something else present" is nitrogen gas; it takes up the "larger proportion" of air. At first glance nitrogen seems uninteresting: it does not burn like hydrogen, does not support combustion like oxygen, has no smell, is not sour, does not dissolve in water, and is neither acidic nor basic. As Faraday says, it is "as indifferent to all our organs as it is possible for a thing to be." We may ask, then "What does it do in air?"

Nitrogen is non-reactive. Its inertness is what makes it so important. If the air were pure oxygen, fire would be uncontrollable. For example, the iron grate in a fireplace "would burn up more powerfully than the coals." Nitrogen gas allows a fire to be more "moderate and useful" and "it takes with it the fumes you have seen produced from the candle." These fumes get carried into the atmosphere, and, as we will discuss in Lecture Five, these fumes, especially carbon dioxide gas,[2] get carried away "to places where they are wanted to perform a great and glorious purpose of good to humankind, for the sustenance of vegetation." Its non-reactiveness is evidenced by the fact that "no action short of the most electric force [such as lightning] ... can cause the nitrogen to combine directly with other elements of the atmosphere." The fact that it is a "perfectly indifferent thing" also means that it is a safe substance.

Faraday turns to the composition of air. It contains 80 percent nitrogen and 20 percent oxygen by volume, with a trace amount of other substances, most notably argon. This means that five liters of air contain about one liter of oxygen and about four liters of nitrogen. This mixture works well "to supply the candle properly with fuel" and "to supply us with an atmosphere which our lungs can healthily and safely breathe." That is, the non-reactive nitrogen contributes the bulk of the air pressure needed.

The masses of these gases are similar but different. Two liters of nitrogen weigh about 2.29 grams and two liters of oxygen weigh about 2.62 grams (at 25°C and 1 atmosphere of pressure). Two liters of air weigh about 2.37 grams. We can see that air has mass by placing two bottles of air on each side of a balance.[3] By using a pump to force air into one of the bottles, we see that this bottle is now heavier because the air has weight. Once we know the density of air we can calculate the weight of air in any room. For example, the amount of air in a large room weighs more than a ton.

Air's weight exerts a pressure of almost 15 pounds per square inch across the Earth's surface. Because air has weight, the air far above the Earth pushes down on the air beneath it, increasing the air pressure below.[4] Next, we turn to eight demonstrations to show that air has weight, is elastic, and is compressible because it is a gas.

- We place our finger over one end of a hollow rubber tube and evacuate the air through the other end. We find that our finger "sticks" to the tube allowing us to lift the tube. This is not because the lack of air is somehow drawing our finger into the tube, but because the pressure of air on the outside is "pushing" our finger onto the tube.

- We evacuate the air from beneath a thin piece of plastic wrap stretched over a funnel until the air pressure above pushes on the plastic wrap, indenting it until it breaks.

- Using a special apparatus we give a human dimension to the weight of air. We bring together two plastic hemispheres to form a hollow sphere. We then remove the air inside this sphere; it is now nearly impossible to pull them apart. The pressure on each square inch of the hemispheres is about 15 pounds. Once the air is let back into the sphere, the hemispheres easily separate.

- On a glass plate we press down on a suction cup, evacuating the air underneath it. Once the air is removed the suction cup will stick tightly to the surface because the air pressure on the outside pushes the suction cup to the surface.

- We fill a glass with water, cover it with a playing card, and turn it upside down. The pressure of the air pushes the card to the cup and the water does not spill.[5]

- We shoot a ball from a popgun, which works by squeezing confined air. The pressure that builds is enough to send a ball out of the gun.

- Using only our breath we blow a hard-boiled egg from one egg cup to another.

- To show that air is compressible; that is, its volume changes as we change the pressure, we place a balloon filled with air into a chamber and evacuate the chamber of air. In this vacuum the balloon expands until it fills the chamber.

The lecture then turns to the "perfectly invisible substance" from the candle. We can place a burning candle under a glass chimney that is open at the bottom and the top and the candle will continue to burn. (See figure on page 78.) We see that moisture appears on the inside of the glass, and this is the water that is formed from the hydrogen in the candle and the oxygen in the air, but we also detect a gas flowing from the chimney. When we test it we find this substance will extinguish a flame; that is, it does not support combustion like oxygen. To determine what this substance is—perhaps it is nitrogen—we collect a sample to test.

We add limewater—a saturated solution of calcium oxide, CaO—to a flask filled with the gas collected from the candle, seal it, and then swirl the solution. The limewater turns milky. When we try this same test with air, the solution stays clear: the "invisible substance," then, is not nitrogen. The solution turns milky because the substance, which is carbon dioxide (CO_2), reacts with the calcium in the limewater to form calcium carbonate, $CaCO_3$, which is chalk.

We can get carbon dioxide from marble, chalks, shells, and corals. For example, if we add hydrochloric acid to marble, we see "a great boiling apparently going on." This "boiling" is the evolution of the carbon dioxide. We test the gas produced to be sure it is carbon dioxide. We observe that it puts out a flame, so it does not support combustion, and it causes limewater to turn milky as did the gas from the candle. These experiments show that no matter how different the methods—from marble or chalk or candle— by which we prepare the carbon dioxide, it is all exactly the same. This echos the point Faraday made in Lecture Three about water—"water, as water, remains always the same"—which shows how science unifies our understanding of the physical world.

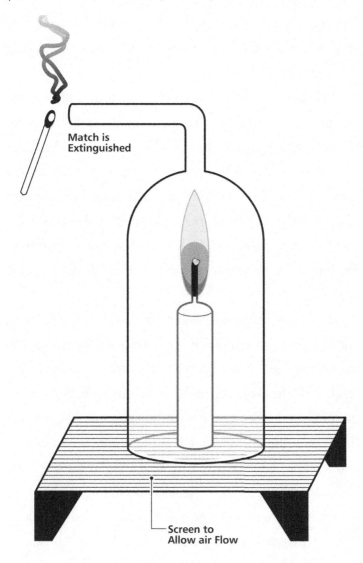

Match is Extinguished

Screen to Allow air Flow

Faraday captures the gases emitted from a candle using a glass jar with a chimney—a glass tube with a right-angle bend. He shows that the flow rate of the gases emitted by the candle are "nearly sufficient to blow" out a match. The match eventually is extinguished because the gases emitted by the candle—including CO_2, and H_2O, which are produced by the chemical reaction in the flame, plus N_2 that entered as part of the incoming air—will not sustain combustion.

The lecture then characterizes some of the physical properties of carbon dioxide. Carbon dioxide does not dissolve much in water—we can collect it over water very easily—and it is a weighty gas, "heavier than the atmosphere." A two liter sample of carbon dioxide (at 1 atmosphere and 25°C) has a mass of 3.60 g while that of hydrogen is 0.16 g, oxygen is 2.62 g, nitrogen is 2.29 g, and air is 2.37 g. We see that carbon dioxide is more dense than air because we can take a flask of carbon dioxide and pour the gas into another container filled with air. The carbon dioxide displaces the air. Although the gas is invisible we test that it is there by showing that it puts out a flame. We blow air-filled soap bubbles into a tank filled with carbon dioxide and see that the bubbles float because carbon dioxide is more dense than air.

In the next and final lecture we examine carbon dioxide in more detail and this exploration allows us to see an analogy between the burning of the candle and respiration.

Notes

1. Faraday tested for the presence of oxygen using nitrous oxide. This colorless gas when brought in contact with oxygen, unites with it, and forms hyponitrous acid, $H_2N_2O_2$, which is red. Nitrous oxide is, today, a controlled substance: it is the "laughing gas" used by some dentists.

2. Faraday's name for carbon dioxide was carbonic acid.

3. Here we technically are looking at masses by using a balance, but air, and all gases, have weight as well. Faraday, in his lectures, uses

"weight" and "mass" interchangeably, although weight is a force due to gravity, and mass is the amount of a substance.

4. Observe, for example, that air pressure in the mountains is lower than that at sea level.

5. Cohesive and adhesive effects also hold the card to the water, but the weight of the water is overcome by the pressure of the air.

THE NATURE OF THE ATMOSPHERE

WE HAVE NOW SEEN that we can produce hydrogen and oxygen from the water that we obtained from the candle. Hydrogen, you know, comes from the candle, and oxygen, you believe, comes from the air. But then you have a right to ask me, "How is it that the air and the oxygen do not equally well burn the candle?" If you remember what happened when I put a jar of oxygen over a piece of candle, you recollect that there was a very different kind of combustion to that which takes place in the air. Why is this? It is a very important question, and one I shall endeavor to make you understand: it relates most intimately to the nature of the atmosphere, and it's most important to us.

We have several tests for oxygen besides the mere

burning of bodies. You've seen a candle burnt in oxygen, or in the air. But we have other tests besides these, and I am about to show you one of them for the purpose of carrying your conviction and your experience further. It is a very curious and useful one.

I have here a flask half-filled with a solution of potassium hydroxide, glucose, and methylene blue indicator and filled the rest of the way with oxygen gas. I shake the flask and the oxygen mixes with the solution. "What happens?" say you, "they together produce no such combustion as was seen in the case of the candle." But see how the presence of oxygen is told by its association with these other substances. What a beautiful-colored solution I have obtained in this way, showing me the presence of the oxygen! In the same way we can try this experiment by mixing common air with this solution. Here is another flask containing the same solution, but this time with air above it. I shake this flask and you see the result: the solution turns blue, and that shows me that there is oxygen in the air—the very same substance that had been already obtained by us from the water produced by the candle. But then, beyond that, how is it that the candle does not burn in air as well as in oxygen? We will come to that point at once. The solutions react with the gas, and the appearance to the eye is alike in both, and I cannot tell which of these flasks contains oxygen and which contains air, although I know they have been previously filled with these gases. In order to examine whether there is any difference between them we simply need to wait. Notice how the blue color of the solution fades in this flask, the flask with air. Why is that? Because there is in air, besides oxygen, something else present. The solution left something untouched—there is, in fact, a gas in air, which the solution cannot touch, and this gas is not oxygen, and yet is part of the atmosphere.

So that is one way of opening out air into the two things of which it is composed—oxygen, which burns our candles, or anything else; and this other substance—nitrogen—which will not burn them. This other part of the air is by far the larger proportion, and it is a very curious body, when we come to examine it; it is remarkably curious, and yet you say, perhaps, that it is very uninteresting. It is uninteresting in some respects because of this—that it shows no brilliant effects of combustion. If I test it with a taper as I do oxygen and hydrogen, it does not burn like hydrogen, nor does it make the taper burn like oxygen. It has no smell; it is not sour; it does not dissolve in water; it is neither an acid nor an alkali; it is as indifferent to all our organs as it is possible for a thing to be.

And you might say, "It is nothing; it is not worth chemical attention; what does it do in the air?" Ah! then come our beautiful and fine results shown us by an observant philosophy. Suppose, in place of having nitrogen, or nitrogen and oxygen, we had pure oxygen as our atmosphere; what would become of us? A piece of iron lit in a jar of oxygen, for example, goes on burning to the end. When you see a fire in an iron grate, imagine where the grate would go to if the whole of the atmosphere were oxygen. The grate would burn up more powerfully than the coals—for the iron of the grate itself is even more combustible than the coals which we burn in it. A fire put into the middle of a locomotive would be a fire in a magazine of fuel, if the atmosphere were oxygen. The nitrogen lowers it down and makes it moderate and useful for us, and then, with all that, it takes away with it the fumes that you have seen produced from the candle, disperses them throughout the whole of the atmosphere, and carries them away to places where they are wanted to perform a great and glorious purpose of good to humankind, for the sustenance of vegetation; and thus does a most wonderful work, although you say, on examining it, "Why, it is a perfectly indifferent thing." This nitrogen in its ordinary state is an inactive element; no action short of the most intense electric force, and then in the most infinitely small degree, can cause the nitrogen to combine directly with other elements of the atmosphere, or with other things round it; it is a perfectly indifferent, and therefore to say, a safe substance.

But before I take you to that result, I must tell you about the atmosphere itself. Here is a composition of one hundred parts of atmospheric air:

COMPOSITION OF AIR[*]

	by volume	by mass
oxygen	20.9%	22.3%
nitrogen	78.1%	77.7%

Plus traces of argon and other gases

It is a true analysis of the atmosphere, so far as regards the quantity of oxygen and the quantity of nitrogen present. By our analysis, we find that five liters of the atmosphere contain only one liter of oxygen, and four liters of nitrogen by bulk. That is our analysis of the atmosphere. It requires all that quantity of nitrogen to reduce the oxygen down, so as to be able to supply the candle properly with fuel, so as to supply us with an atmosphere which our lungs can healthily and safely breathe; for it is just as important to make the oxygen right for us to breathe, as it is to make the atmosphere right for the burning of the fire and the candle. First of all, let me tell you the weight of these gases. Two liters of nitrogen weighs roughly 2.29 grams. The oxygen is heavier: two liters of it weigh about 2.62 grams. Two liters of air weigh about 2.37 grams.

You might ask "How do you weigh gases?" I will show you; it is very simple, and easily done. Here is a balance, and here is a plastic bottle. This bottle is balanced by the weight of the other bottle. And here is a pump by which we can force the air into the bottle, and with it we will force in a certain number of volumes of air. Now, see how it sinks: it is much heavier than it was. By what? By the air that we have forced into it by the pump. There is not a greater volume of air, but there is the same volume of heavier air, because we have forced in air upon it. This bulk of air weighs about two and a half grams. It is wonderful how it accumulates when you come to larger volumes. I have calculated the weight of air in this room—you would hardly imagine it, but it is above a ton. So rapidly do the weights rise up, and so important is the presence of the atmosphere, and of the oxygen and the nitrogen in it, and the use it performs in conveying things to and fro from place to place, and carrying bad vapors to places where they will do good instead of harm.

Having given you that little illustration with respect to the weight of the air, let me show you certain consequences of it. When I put my finger on this tube and remove the air look at what happens. Why is my finger fastened to this tube, and why am I able to pull the hose about? It is the weight of the air—the weight of the air that is above. I have another experiment here, which I think will explain to you more about it.

When air is pumped from underneath the plastic which is stretched over the funnel, you will see the effect in another shape: the top is quite flat at present, but I will make a very little motion with the pump, and now look at it—see how it has gone down, see how it is bent in. You will see the plastic go in more and more, until at last I expect it will be driven in and broken by the force of the atmosphere pressing upon it. Now, that was done entirely by the weight of the air pressing on it, and you can easily understand how that is. The particles that are piled up in the atmosphere stand upon each other, as these five cubes do. You can easily conceive that four of these five cubes are resting upon the bottom one, and if I take that away, the others will all sink down. So it is with the atmosphere: the air that is above is sustained by the air that is beneath; and when the air is pumped away from beneath them, the change occurs which you saw when I placed my finger on the air-pump, and which you saw in the case of the plastic, and which you shall see better in the next demonstration.

It is a little apparatus of two hollow plastic hemispheres, closely fitted together, and having an outlet, through which we can exhaust the air from the inside; and although the two halves are so easily taken apart, while the air is left within, yet you will see, when we exhaust it by-and-by, I will be unable to pull them apart. Every square inch of surface that is contained in the area of this vessel sustains fifteen pounds by weight, or nearly so, when the air is taken out.

Here is another very pretty thing: a suction cup. If I clap it upon the glass you see at once it holds. I can easily slip it about, and if I pull it up, it pulls the glass plate with it. Only when I lift the edge can I get it off. Why does it hold? It is only kept down by the pressure of the atmosphere above. I have a second one and if I press them together, you'll see how firmly they stick. And, indeed, we may use them as they are proposed to be used, to stick against windows, or against walls, where they will adhere for an evening, and serve to hang anything on them that you want.

Next is an experiment that you can do at home; it is a very pretty illustration of the pressure of the atmosphere. The popgun will confine the air that is within the tube perfectly and completely for our purpose. The confined air will drive the front ball out with a force something like that of gunpowder; for gunpowder is in part dependent upon the same action as this popgun.

I saw the other day an experiment which pleased me much, as I thought it would serve our purpose here. By the proper application of air I expect to be able to drive this egg out of one cup into the other by the force of my breath; but if I fail, it is in a good cause; and I do not promise success, because I have been talking more than I ought to make the experiment succeed.

You see that the air which I blew went downward between the egg and the cup, and made a blast under the egg, and is thus able to lift a heavy thing—for a full egg is a very heavy thing for air to lift. If you want to make the experiment, you had better boil the egg quite hard first, and then you may very safely try to blow it from one cup to the other, with a little care.

I have now kept you long enough upon this property of the weight of the air, but there is another thing I should like to mention. You saw the way in which, in the popgun, I was able to drive the second yellow ball a half or two-thirds of an inch before the first ball started, by virtue of the elasticity of the air—just as I pressed into the plastic bottle the particles of air by means of a pump; now, this depends upon a wonderful property in the air, namely, its compressibility; and I should like to give you a good demonstration of this. If I take anything that confines the air properly, as does this balloon, which also is able to contract and expand so as to give us a measure of the elasticity of the air, and confine in the balloon a certain portion of air; and then, if we take the atmosphere off with this pump—just as in the cases we put the pressure on—if we take the pressure off, you will see how it will then go on expanding and expanding, larger and larger, until it will fill the whole of this jar.

We will now turn to another very important part of our subject, remembering that we have examined the candle in its burning, and have found that it gives rise to various products. We have the products, you know, of soot, of water, and of something else which you have not yet examined. We have collected the water, but have allowed the other things to go into the air. Let us now examine some of these other products.

Here is an experiment which I think will help you in part in this way. First, we put our candle under a chimney. My candle will go on burning, because the air passage is open at the bottom and the top. You see the moisture appearing—that you already know about. It is water produced from the candle by the action of the air upon the hydrogen. But, besides that, something is going out at the top: it is not moisture—it is not water—it is not condensible; and yet, after all, it has very singular properties. You will find that the gas coming out of the top of our chimney is nearly sufficient to blow the light out I am holding to it; and if I put the light fairly opposed to the current, it will blow it quite out. You will say that is as it should be because the nitrogen does not support combustion, and ought to put the match out, since the match will not burn in nitrogen. But is there nothing else there than nitrogen? I must now anticipate—that is to say, I must use my own knowledge to supply you with the means that we adopt for the purpose of ascertaining these things, and examining such gases as these. If I hold an empty flask to this chimney, I shall capture the combustion of the candle below; we shall soon find that this flask contains not merely a gas that is bad as regards the combustion of a taper put into it, but having other properties.

If I take some of this beautiful clear limewater, and pour it into this flask, which has collected the gas from the candle, you will see a change come about. You see that the water has become quite milky. Observe, this will not happen with air merely. Here is a flask filled with air; and if I put a little limewater into it, neither the oxygen nor the nitrogen, nor anything else that is in that quantity of air, will make any change in the limewater. It remains perfectly clear, and no shaking of that quantity of limewater with that quantity of air in its common state will cause any change.

This is chalk, consisting of the lime in the limewater, combined with something that came from the candle—that other product which we are in search of, and which I want to tell you about today. This is a substance made visible to us by its action, which is not the action of the limewater either upon the oxygen or upon the nitrogen, nor upon the water itself, but it is something new to us from the candle. But we have a better means of getting this substance, and in greater quantity, so as to ascertain what its general characteristics are.

We can produce this substance in great abundance from a multitude of unexpected sources. All limestones can produce a great deal of this gas which issues from the candle, and which we call carbon dioxide. All chalks, all shells, all corals can also make a great quantity of this curious gas. We can easily evolve carbon dioxide from marble.

Here is a jar containing some hydrochloric acid, and here is a taper which, if I put it into that jar, will show only the presence of common air. There is, you see, pure air down to the bottom; the jar is full of it. Here is a substance—marble, a very beautiful and superior marble—and if I put that piece into the jar, a great boiling apparently goes on. That, however, is not steam—it is a gas that is rising up; and if I now search the jar by a taper I shall have exactly the same effect produced upon the taper as I had from the gas which issued from the end of the chimney over the burning candle. It is exactly the same action, and caused by the very same substance that issued from the candle; and in this way we can get carbon dioxide in great abundance—we have already nearly filled the jar. We also find that this gas is not merely contained in marble. Here is some common chalk and in this flask more hydrochloric acid. It too evolves carbon dioxide, exactly the same in its nature and properties as the gas we obtained from the combustion of the candle in the atmosphere. And no matter how different the methods—from marble or chalk or candle—by which we prepare this carbon dioxide, you will see, when we get to the end of our subject, that it is all exactly the same, whether prepared in the one way or another. We will now proceed to the next experiment with regard to carbon dioxide. What is its nature?

Here is a vessel full of carbon dioxide, and we will try it, as we have done so many other gases, by combustion. You see it is not combustible, nor does it support combustion.

Neither, as we know, does it dissolve much in water, because we collect it over water very easily. Then, you know that it has an effect, and becomes white in contact with limewater; and when it does become white in that way, it becomes one of the constituents to make carbonate of lime or limestone.

It is a very weighty gas—it is heavier than the atmosphere. I have put their respective weights at the lower part of this table, along with, for comparison, the weights of the other gases we have been examining:

MASS IN GRAMS OF TWO LITERS
OF VARIOUS GASES*

hydrogen	0.16
nitrogen	2.29
air	2.37
oxygen	2.62
carbon dioxide	3.60

*at 1 ATM and 298 K

Two liters of this weighs about 3.6 grams. You can see by some experiments that this is a heavy gas. I have a flask contain dry ice that is subliming and thus pushing out the air, replacing it with carbon dioxide. I'll pour a little of this carbon dioxide into another flask filled with nothing but air. I wonder whether any has gone in or not. I cannot tell by the appearance, but I can in this way. It extinguishes the flame; if I were to examine it by limewater I would find it by that test also. Next is an experiment where I will show you its density.

If I blow soap bubbles, which of course are filled with air, into this container filled with carbon dioxide, they will float. They are floating by virtue of the greater density of the carbon dioxide than of the air. And now, having so far given you the history of carbon dioxide—as to its sources in the candle, as to its physical properties and density—in the next lecture I shall show you of what it is composed, and where it gets its elements from.

RESPIRATION & ITS ANALOGY TO THE BURNING OF A CANDLE

Key points of the lecture

- Carbon dioxide is made by the combining of carbon from the candle and oxygen from the air.

- Burning wood also gives off carbon dioxide. The black "charcoal" left after burning is the carbon in wood that has been incompletely burned

- Most solids, for example iron, burn to form a new solid. Carbon, in contrast, burns to form a gas. This allows for the products to be carried away during combustion as in a fireplace or a candle.

- The respiration in humans is analogous to the combustion of a candle. In a candle the wax is a fuel containing carbon, this carbon reacts with

oxygen to form carbon dioxide; the fuel for us
is carbohydrates, often sugar, which contains
carbon that reacts with oxygen from the air we
breath to form carbon dioxide, which we then
exhale.

- The reaction time for a chemical change to occur
  varies greatly; it depends on the starting materials and the conditions, such as temperature.

- The animal and plant kingdoms are linked by
  carbon dioxide. All animals take in oxygen and
  release carbon dioxide, while plants do the opposite.

In this lecture Faraday investigates the chemical makeup
of carbon dioxide. He starts his investigation by reviewing
what we learned in previous lectures. We learned in Lecture
Four that the candle gives off carbon dioxide gas, which will
turn a limewater solution milky white because the carbon
dioxide turns into calcium carbonate. Calcium carbonate
can be turned back into carbon dioxide by reacting chalk,
shells, corals, and many other rocks with acid.

Faraday next gives the "chemical history" of carbon
dioxide. By this he means revealing "the elements of the
carbon dioxide supplied by the candle." While the make-up
of carbon dioxide may be obvious from its present-day name,
in Faraday's time it was called carbonic acid. The name,
while perhaps implying carbon, does not immediately tell

us only carbon and oxygen are present. The term carbonic acid was used because carbon dioxide can be dissolved in water to create an acidic solution. He starts by showing us that the carbon from the candle goes into the carbon dioxide emitted by a candle. We saw earlier that a candle that "burns badly" produces smoke and that the brightness of the flame is due to the smoke becoming ignited. That is, if the smoke,which contains carbon particles produced from the candle wax, is not released but remains in the flame it gives us a "beautiful light." Faraday tests this with a large flame that is "extravagant in its burning." He puts some lighter fluid on a sponge and lights it. Black smoke rises from the sponge because there is a lot of carbon in the fuel and there is not enough oxygen in the air to react with it—this is the incomplete combustion noted in earlier lectures. Faraday then places the burning sponge into a container with more oxygen than in air and notes "that the smoke is all consumed." The carbon that was making the black smoke is "entirely burned in this oxygen, exactly as in the combustion of the candle" and this makes the bright flame as we discussed in Lecture Two. The carbon that does burn comes out as carbon dioxide but if there is not enough oxygen, the carbon is "thrown off in excess" and we see the black smoke.

Carbon dioxide is a compound, meaning it is made up of more than one type of element. Thus it is a "body that we ought to be able to take asunder," or separate into its elements, much as we did with water. To do this we will find a chemical method to release the oxygen; to react it with an element "that can attract the oxygen from it and leave the carbon behind." To test if oxygen is released we will see if we can burn something. We already know that carbon dioxide does not support combustion, and we showed that it extinguishes flame. Oxygen, though, does support combustion. This is important because Faraday will show that a flame can be sustained by liberating oxygen from carbon dioxide.

To release the oxygen from carbon dioxide we react magnesium metal with dry ice.[1] Dry ice is carbon dioxide in solid form; it has a temperature of −109.3°F or −78.5°C. We start the magnesium burning using a torch and then cover the metal completely with dry ice. As the magnesium burns the light emitted becomes brighter and brighter. Recall that in Lecture Three we saw that a candle burned brighter in oxygen than in air. This implies that the magnesium here burns in an atmosphere that contains more and more oxygen—oxygen is being created or released. To verify this we study the remnants left over from the reaction: a white powder, which is magnesium oxide (MgO), and also what Faraday calls a "common black substance." Clearly this is carbon. We've shown that carbon dioxide, as the name implies, consists of carbon and oxygen. We can say then, that "whenever carbon burns under common circumstances, it produces carbon dioxide."

We can test this idea that whenever carbon burns it produces carbon dioxide by burning a piece of wood and then collecting the gas released in a container with limewater. Indeed we see the same milky product that we saw when doing this with carbon dioxide. Being careful scientists we also test an unburned piece of wood: it does not make limewater milky. We see, now, that the burning of wood produces carbon dioxide, just like the burning of a candle. We can also see that if we partly burn a piece of wood by blowing out the flame before it all burns, carbon is present as evidenced by the characteristic black charring. And while we don't see this black charring with a candle or a Bunsen burner we do see evidence that carbon is released. The brightness is evidence, says Faraday, that "there is carbon in the flame."

Next we make an important distinction between various types of fuels. The members of the carbonaceous, or carbon-containing, series (coals, charcoals, woods) start as a solid and, when burned, become a gas. This is different from substances such as iron which will burn to form a new solid. If all fuels were like iron we "could not then have such a combustion as you have in a fireplace."

The lecture turns next to a stunning analogy: there is a relationship between "the combustion of a candle and that living kind of combustion which goes on within us," which is respiration. "In every one of us there is a living process of combustion going on very similar to that of a candle," Faraday suggests, adding that this is "not merely true in a poetical sense, the relation of the life of humans to a candle." The lecture elaborates on this analogy, but the essence is this: a candle uses oxygen from air to produce carbon dioxide, water, and heat from wax, which serves as a carbon-based fuel; in the human body we take in oxygen from the air, convert it inside our bodies to carbon dioxide, water, and heat by reacting oxygen with food, which is a carbon-based fuel for our bodies.

The lecture turns to a set of experiments that make "the relation very plain." In the first experiment a burning candle is placed in an apparatus with an air inlet at the bottom and limited air flow at the top. The candle continues to burn because air is drawn through the tube connected to the air inlet. If the air inlet is blocked combustion stops: no oxygen is available for combustion. Next Faraday gently exhales into the tube so the gas flows around the candle but does not blow it out. "The result," Faraday, notes is "that the light [goes] out for want of oxygen and for no other reason." Our lungs, therefore take "the oxygen out of the air" and so there is not enough oxygen "to supply the combustion of the candle."

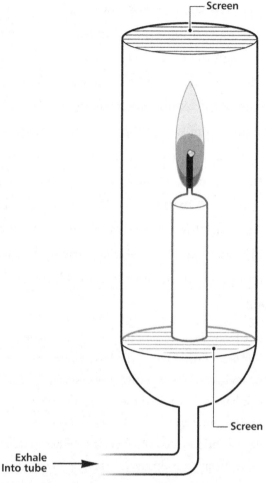

Faraday uses this apparatus to demonstrate that gases humans exhale won't sustain combustion. He breathes gently into the lower tube, so that his breath won't blow out the candle directly. As the exhaled gases surround the flame, it flickers and then goes out. Faraday shows later in this lecture that these exhaled gases contain CO_2 like the gases emitted by a candle.

To investigate what happens to the oxygen we test our breath with limewater using a special vessel. By drawing in external air through the limewater we see "no effect upon the water; it does not make the limewater turbid"; that is, as we have seen, air does not affect limewater. But if we blow into the limewater we see the water turn "white and milky" showing that we are breathing out carbon dioxide.

The lecture then explains why this process of respiration—the taking in of oxygen and the release of carbon dioxide—is necessary for our survival. "If we restrain our respiration," Faraday says, "we should destroy ourselves." Faraday then explains, at the most basic level, the process of respiration:[2]

> We consume food: the food goes through that strange set of vessels and organs within us, and is brought into various parts of the body, into the digestive parts especially. The air that we inhale is drawn into the lungs, absorbed into the bloodstream, and transported throughout the body so that the oxygen and the food come close together. In the body a curious, wonderful change takes place: the oxygen combines with the carbon (not carbon in a free state, but as in this case placed ready for action at the moment), and makes carbon dioxide, and is so thrown out into the atmosphere, and thus this singular result takes place. The oxygen can thus act upon the food, producing precisely the same results in kind as we have seen in the case of the candle. The candle combines with parts of the air, forming carbon dioxide and evolves heat; we may thus look upon the food as fuel.

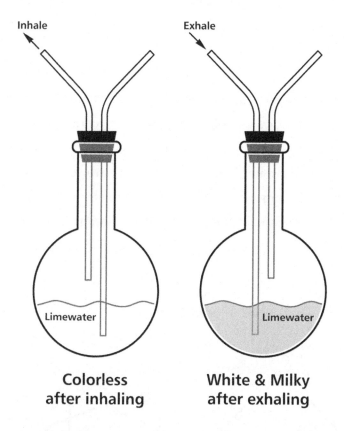

Colorless after inhaling   **White & Milky after exhaling**

Faraday uses this apparatus to show that human breath contains CO_2. **a** *Faraday draws in a breath through the limewater: he observes no change in the limewater.* **b** *He rotates the apparatus and exhales into the limewater: it now turns cloudy. Limewater turns cloudy, as he showed in an earlier lecture, when CO_2 gas is bubbled through it.*

Sugar, for example, is a carbon containing compound. The formula for table sugar is $C_{12}H_{22}O_{11}$, which can be written as $C_{12}(H_2O)_{11}$, showing us why sugar is called a carbohydrate—that is, containing carbon, hydrogen and oxygen, where the hydrogen and oxygen are in a 2:1 ratio as in water.

The lecture demonstrates that sugar contains carbon by adding sulfuric acid to it. In essence the sulfuric acid removes the water, leaving behind a black tower of carbon. The carbon in sugars that we eat combines with oxygen that we breathe in the process of respiration "making us like candles."

Sucrose
(table sugar)
$C_{12}H_{22}O_{11}$

Table sugar has the formula $C_{12}H_{22}O_{11}$. Faraday notes that this can be rewritten as $C_{12}(H_2O)_{11}$, which shows us why sugar is called a carbohydrate: it contains carbon, hydrogen and oxygen, where the hydrogen and oxygen are in a 2:1 ratio as in water.

The lecture then alludes to the differing rates of reaction. In Lecture Two when we oxidized sugar with potassium chlorate the reaction was very quick, but the result, the formation of carbon dioxide and heat, is similar to respiration. This reaction, though, is "different from respiration in its form but not in its kind." That is, "what occurs in [the] lungs, taking in oxygen from another source, namely the atmosphere, takes place between potassium chlorate and sugar by a more rapid process." We have also seen how quickly potassium reacts with water: "the moment the potassium was brought to the water, it acted." When we breathe or when we burn a candle, this chemical affinity, this "attraction of the different parts one to the other is going on." A difference, though, is while the potassium starts into action with water at once, the carbon in the candle "will remain days, weeks, months, or years in the presence of air." Different substances will react at different rates. A reaction that we may call spontaneous in that it will occur does not mean that the reaction will occur immediately; "some will wait till the temperature is raised a little, and others till it is raised a good deal." The lecture shows the difference by comparing gunpowder and gun cotton when we apply a heated glass rod to each. The gun cotton reacts immediately, "but not even the hottest part of the rod is now hot enough to fire the gunpowder."

In contrast, the process of respiration waits no time.

Once the air enters when we breathe, it "unites with the carbon. Even in the lowest temperature which the body can bear short of being frozen, the action begins at once, producing the carbon dioxide of respiration, and so all things go on fitly and properly."

In contrast, the candle can remain in the presence of air for years without reacting, but once it begins to burn it can burn for hours. This leads to a great deal of carbon dioxide released into the atmosphere. The same can be said for respiration. A person can convert as much as 200 grams, almost half of a pound, of carbon into carbon dioxide in a day; a cow will convert about 2,000 grams of carbon, almost five pounds, and a horse about 2,200 grams of carbon each day, solely by respiration. The act of respiration, Faraday reveals, is the process in which mammals "get their warmth … by the conversion of carbon, not in a free state, but in a state of combination." This amounts to over a million tons of carbon dioxide formed from human respiration each day going "up into the air." It is fortunate, then, that the product of carbon combustion is a gas because if, like iron, the product were solid, respiration "could not go on." As charcoal burns, the gaseous carbon dioxide goes "into the atmosphere which is the great vehicle, the great carrier for conveying it away to other places." What becomes of this carbon dioxide?

As we saw earlier in the lecture, a candle flame cannot

be sustained in our breath due to the carbon dioxide. Similarly, the carbon dioxide is "injurious to us, for we cannot breathe air twice over." However, carbon dioxide "is the very life and support of plants and vegetables that grow upon the surface of the earth." Thus, the plants require this carbon dioxide. Using this observation Faraday returns in his closing remarks to his grand theme: how science unifies all physical phenomena. Plants use this carbon dioxide during photosynthesis and return oxygen necessary for human survival. This cycle occurs in the water as well, as fish "and other animals respire upon the same principle" although "fish respire by the oxygen which is dissolved from the air by the water." This cycle makes "the animal and vegetable kingdoms subservient to each other and all the plants growing upon the surface of the earth." Leaves on a tree, for example could not live in "pure air," but "give them carbon with other matters, and they live and rejoice." And in doing so, they give us back the oxygen we have used to form carbon dioxide.

Faraday ends with a call to action:

Indeed, all I can say to you at the end of these lectures (for we must come to an end at one time or other) is to express a wish that you may, in your generation, be fit to compare to a candle; that you may, like it, shine as lights to those about you; that, in all your actions, you may justify the beauty of the taper by making your deeds honorable and effectual in the discharge of your duty to humankind.

Notes

1. Faraday ignited a piece of potassium in an atmosphere of carbon dioxide. Here we replaced the oxidant, using magnesium instead of potassium, and instead of using carbon dioxide gas we used dry ice, which is solid carbon dioxide. Faraday's original experiment is dangerous: when he performed it in the lecture the potassium exploded.

2. We modified Faraday's wording slightly. His lecture implies that the chemical reaction occurs in the lungs. His original words were: "We consume food: the food goes through that strange set of vessels and organs within us, and is brought into various parts of the system, into the digestive parts especially; and alternately the portion which is so changed is carried through our lungs by one set of vessels, while the air that we inhale and exhale is drawn into and thrown out of the lungs by another set of vessels, so that the air and the food come close together, separated only by an exceedingly thin surface: the air can thus act upon the blood by this process, producing precisely the same results in kind as we have seen in the case of the candle. The candle combines with parts of the air, forming carbonic acid, and evolves heat; so in the lungs there is this curious, wonderful change taking place. The air entering, combines with the carbon (not carbon in a free state, but, as in this case, placed ready for action at the moment), and makes carbonic acid, and is so thrown out into the atmosphere, and thus this singular result takes place: we may thus look upon the food as fuel."

RESPIRATION & ITS ANALOGY
TO THE BURNING OF A CANDLE

I TOLD YOU, WHEN WE LAST MET, a good deal about carbon dioxide. We found, by the limewater test, that when the vapor from the top of the candle was received into bottles, and tested by a solution of limewater (the composition of which I explained to you, and which you can make for yourselves), we had that the white opacity which was in fact calcareous matter, like shells and corals, and many of the rocks and minerals in the earth. But I have not yet told you fully and clearly the chemical history of this substance—carbon dioxide—as we have it from the candle, and I must now resume that subject. We have seen the products, and the nature of them, as they issue from the candle. We have traced the water to its elements, and now we have to see where are the elements of the carbon dioxide supplied by the candle. A few experiments will show you this.

You remember that when a candle burns badly, it produces smoke; but if it is burning well, there is *no* smoke. And you know that the brightness of the candle is due to this smoke, which becomes ignited. Here is an experiment to prove this.

So long as the smoke remains in the flame of the candle and becomes ignited, it gives a beautiful light, and never appears to us in the form of black particles. I will light some fuel, which is extravagant in its burning. This will serve our purpose—a little lighter fluid on a sponge. You see the smoke rising from it, and floating into the air in large quantities; and, remember now, the carbon dioxide that we have from the candle is from such smoke as that. To make that evident to you, I will introduce this into a container where I have plenty of oxygen, the rich part of the atmosphere. You now see that the smoke is all consumed. The carbon which you saw flying off from the lighter fluid flame in the air is now entirely burned in this oxygen, exactly as in the combustion of the candle. All the carbon which is burned in oxygen, or air, comes out as carbon dioxide, while those particles which are not so burned show you the second substance in the carbon dioxide—namely, the carbon—that body which made the flame so bright while there was plenty of air, but which was thrown off in excess when there was not oxygen enough to burn it.

There is another experiment which I must give you before you are fully acquainted with the general nature of carbon dioxide. Being a compound body, consisting of carbon and oxygen, carbon dioxide is a body that we ought to be able to take asunder, and so we can. As we did with water, so we can with carbon dioxide—take the two parts asunder. The simplest and quickest way is to act upon the carbon dioxide by a substance that can attract the oxygen from it, and leave the carbon behind. You recollect that I took potassium and put it upon water or ice, and you saw that it could take the oxygen from the hydrogen. Now, suppose we do something of the same kind here with this carbon dioxide.

Now, let me take some magnesium turnings and get them to act upon carbon dioxide in the form of dry ice. If we apply heat to the magnesium, you will see that it can burn in carbon dioxide; and it's very burning is proof of the existence of oxygen in the carbon dioxide. In addition to a brilliant light, you will see what is left behind.

We find that, besides the white powder formed, which is magnesium oxide, there is a quantity of carbon produced; carbon obtained from the carbon dioxide, as a common black substance; so that you have the entire proof of the nature of carbon dioxide as consisting of carbon and oxygen. And now, I may tell you, that whenever carbon burns under common circumstances, it produces carbon dioxide.

Suppose I take this piece of wood, and put it in a bottle with limewater. I might shake that water up with wood and the atmosphere as long as I pleased, it would still remain clear as you see it; but suppose I burn the piece of wood in the air of that bottle. You, of course, know that I get water. Do I get carbon dioxide? There it is, the carbonate lime, which results from carbon dioxide, and that carbon dioxide must be formed from the carbon which comes from the wood, from the candle, or any other thing. Indeed, you have yourselves tried a very pretty experiment, by which you see the carbon in wood. If you take a piece of wood and partly burn it and then blow it out you have carbon left. Here is the piece of wood, that I partly burnt, you see the carbon left on it. A candle does not show it, nor does a Bunsen burner, but both contain carbon. You see no carbon when they burn, but you see a flame; and because it is bright, it will lead you to guess that there is carbon in the flame. I hope that by these experiments you will learn to see when carbon is present, and understand what are the products of combustion, when gas or other bodies are thoroughly burned in the air.

Before we leave the subject of carbon, let us make a few experiments and remarks upon its wonderful condition as respects ordinary combustion. I have shown you that

the carbon in burning burns only as a solid body, and yet
you perceive that, after it is burned, it ceases to be a solid.
There are very few fuels that act like this. It is, in fact,
only that great source of fuel, the carbonaceous series, the
coals, charcoals, and woods, that can do it. I do not know
that there is any other elementary substance besides carbon
that burns with these conditions; and if it had not been so,
what would happen to us? Suppose all fuel had been like
iron, which, when it burns, burns into a solid substance.
We could not then have such a combustion as you have
in a fireplace.

Now, I must take you to a very interesting part of our
subject—to the relation between the combustion of a candle
and that living kind of combustion which goes on within
us. In every one of us there is a living process of combustion
going on very similar to that of a candle; and I must try to
make that plain to you. For it is not merely true in a poetical
sense—the relation of the life of humans to a candle; and if
you follow, I think I can make this clear. In order to make
the relation very plain, I have devised a little apparatus with
an air inlet at the bottom and I'll limit the airflow out of the
top with this wire mesh. The lighted candle goes on, you
see, burning very well. You observe that the air which feeds
the flame goes along the horizontal tube and ascends the
vessel. If I stop the aperture through which the air flows,
I stop combustion, as you will perceive. I stop the supply

of air, and consequently the candle goes out. But, now, what will you think of this fact? In a former experiment I showed you the gaseous products going from one burning candle to a flame. If I take the vapor proceeding from another candle, and sent it through this tube, I should put this burning candle out. But what will you say when I tell you that my breath will put out that candle? I do not mean by blowing it out, but simply that the nature of my breath is such that a candle cannot burn in it. I will exhale, and without blowing the flame in any way, let no air enter the tube but what comes from my mouth. You see the result. I did not blow the candle out. I merely let the air which I expired pass into the aperture, and the result was that the light went out for want of oxygen, and for no other reason. My lungs had taken the oxygen out of the air, and there was no more to supply the combustion of the candle. It is, I think, very pretty to see the time it takes before the bad air which I throw into this part of the apparatus has reached the candle. The candle at first goes on burning, but so soon as the air has had time to reach it, it goes out.

To pursue this a little further, let us see what will happen with limewater. Here is a flask which contains a little limewater, and is so arranged as regards the pipes, as to give access to the air within, so that we can ascertain the effect of respired or unrespired air upon it. Of course, I can either draw air in here, and so make the air that feeds my lungs go through the limewater, or I can force the air out of my lungs through this tube, which goes to the bottom, and so shows its effect upon the limewater. You will observe that, however long I draw the external air into the limewater, and then through it to my lungs, I shall produce no effect upon the water. It does not make the limewater turbid but if I throw the air from my lungs through the limewater, several times in succession, you will see how white and milky the water is getting, showing the effect which expired air has upon it. And now you begin to know that the atmosphere which we have spoiled by respiration is spoiled by carbon dioxide, and you see it here in contact with the limewater.

Let us now go a little further. What is all this process going on within us which we cannot do without, either day or night. If we restrain our respiration, as we can to a certain extent, we should destroy ourselves. When we are asleep, the organs of respiration, and the parts that are associated with them, still go on with their action—so necessary is this process of respiration to us, this contact of the air with the lungs.

I must tell you, in the briefest possible manner, what this process is. We consume food: the food goes through that strange set of vessels and organs within us, and is brought into various parts of the body, into the digestive parts especially. The air that we inhale is drawn into the lungs, absorbed into the bloodstream, and transported throughout the body so that the oxygen and the food come close together. In the body a curious, wonderful change takes place: the oxygen combines with the carbon (not carbon in a free state, but, as in this case, placed ready for action at the moment), and makes carbon dioxide, and is so thrown out into the atmosphere, and thus this singular result takes place. The oxygen can thus act upon the food, producing precisely the same results in kind as we have seen in the case of the candle. The candle combines with parts of the air, forming carbon dioxide, and evolves heat; we may thus look upon the food as fuel.

Let us consider sugar, which will serve my purpose. It is a compound of carbon, hydrogen, and oxygen, similar to a candle, as containing the same elements, although not in the same proportion—the proportions being as shown in this table:

SUGAR: $C_{12}H_{22}O_{11}$

PROPORTION OF ELEMENTS BY MASS

carbon (C) 72

hydrogen (H) 11

oxygen (O) 18

This is, indeed a very curious thing, which you can well remember. For the oxygen and hydrogen are in exactly the proportions which form water, so that sugar may be said to be compounded of seventy-two parts of carbon and ninety-nine parts of water; and it is the carbon in the sugar that combines with the oxygen carried in the air by the process of respiration—so making us like candles—producing these actions, warmth, and far more wonderful results besides, for the sustenance of the system, by a most beautiful and simple process. To make this still more striking, let me show you an experiment with a bit of sugar. If I put some sulfuric acid on sugar, it takes away the water, and leaves the carbon in a black mass. You see how the carbon is coming out, and before long we shall have a solid mass of charcoal, all of which has come out of the sugar. Sugar, as you know, is food, and here we have absolutely a solid lump of carbon where you would not have expected it.

Recall that I oxidized sugar in an earlier lecture using potassium chlorate, which is a quicker one than the atmosphere; and different from respiration in its form, though not different in its kind. What occurs in my lungs—taking in oxygen from another source, namely, the atmosphere—takes place between potassium chlorate and sugar by a more rapid process. I also showed you how potassium reacted with water—the moment the potassium was brought to the water, it acted. What a beautiful instance of chemical affinity by which all our operations proceed. When we breathe, the same operation is going on within us. When we burn a candle, the attraction of the different parts one to the other is going on. We have this difference between charcoal and potassium—that, while the potassium can start into action at once, if there be access of water to it, the carbon will remain days, weeks, months, or years in the presence of air.

The manuscripts of Herculaneum were written with carbonaceous ink, and there they have been for almost 2,000 years, not having been at all changed by the atmosphere, though coming in contact with it under various circumstances. Now, what is the circumstance which makes the potassium and carbon differ in this respect? It is a striking thing to see that the matter which is appointed to serve the purpose of fuel waits in its action: it does not start off burning, like the potassium—the carbon waits for action. This waiting is a curious and wonderful thing. Candles do not start into action at once, like the potassium, but there they wait for years, perhaps for ages, without undergoing any alteration. It is curious to see how different substances wait—how some will wait till the temperature is raised a little, and others till it is raised a good deal.

I have here a little gunpowder and some gun-cotton; even these things differ in the conditions under which they will burn. The gunpowder is composed of carbon and other substances, making it highly combustible; and the gun-cotton is another combustible preparation. They are both waiting, but they will start into activity at different degrees of heat, or under different conditions. By applying a heated glass rod to them, we shall see which will start first. You see the gun-cotton has gone off, but not even the hottest part of the rod is now hot enough to fire the gunpowder. How beautifully that shows you the differences in the degree in which bodies act in this way! In the one case the substances will wait any time until the associated bodies are made active by heat; but in the other, as in the process of respiration, it waits no time. The air that enters when we breath unites with the carbon; even in the lowest temperatures which the body can bear short of being frozen, the action begins at once, producing the carbon dioxide of respiration: and so all things go on fitly and properly.

You will be astonished when I tell you what this curious play of carbon amounts to. A candle will burn some four, five, six, or seven hours. What, then, must be the daily amount of carbon going up into the air in the way of carbon dioxide? What a quantity of carbon must go from each of us in respiration! What a wonderful change of carbon must take place under these circumstances of combustion or respiration! A person in twenty-four hours converts as much as 200 grams of carbon into carbon dioxide; a dairy cow will convert 2,000 grams, and a horse 2,200, solely by the act of respiration. That is, the horse in twenty-four hours burns 2,200 grams of charcoal, or carbon, in his organs of respiration, to supply his natural warmth in that time. All the warm-blooded animals get their warmth in this way, by the conversion of carbon, not in a free state, but in a state of combination. And what an extraordinary notion this gives us of the alterations going on in our atmosphere. As much as one and a half million tons of carbon dioxide is formed by human respiration in the world in twenty-four hours. And where does all this go? Up into the air. If the carbon had been like iron which, in burning, produces a solid substance, what would happen? Combustion could not go on. As charcoal burns, it becomes a vapor and passes off into the atmosphere, which is the great vehicle, the great carrier for conveying it away to other places. Then, what becomes of it? Wonderful it is to find that the change produced by respiration, which seems so injurious to us (for we cannot breathe air twice over), is the very life and support of plants and vegetables that grow upon the surface of the earth. It is the same also under the surface, in the great bodies of water; for fishes and other animals respire upon the same principle, though not exactly by contact with the open air.

Fish respire by the oxygen which is dissolved from the air by the water, and form carbon dioxide; and they all move about to produce the one great work of making the animal and vegetable kingdoms subservient to each other. And all the plants growing upon the surface of the earth absorb carbon. These leaves are taking up their carbon from the atmosphere, to which we have given it in the form of carbon dioxide, and they are growing and prospering. Give them a pure air like ours, and they could not live in it; give them carbon with other matter, and they live and rejoice. This tree, as do all plants, gets its carbon from the atmosphere, which, as we have seen, carries away what is bad for us and at the same time good for them—what is disease to the one being health to the other. So are we made dependent, not merely upon our fellow-creatures, but upon our fellow-existers, all Nature being tied together by the laws that make one part conduce to the good of another.

Indeed, all I can say to you at the end of these lectures (for we must come to an end at one time or other) is to express a wish that you may, in your generation, be fit to compare to a candle; that you may, like it, shine as lights to those about you; that, in all your actions, you may justify the beauty of the taper by making your deeds honorable and effectual in the discharge of your duty to humankind.

A NOTE ON THE TEACHING GUIDE

Michael Faraday aimed his lectures toward those new to science, especially young people. He choose a candle to attract this younger audience: it was commonplace, but off limits. Every household had candles, yet how tantalizing a candle must have been for a young child in the nineteenth century. Although candles are not as commonplace today—most children see them only at birthday or holiday celebrations—a burning candle still fascinates any child. It can be used by teachers to guide students through the scientific method and as an entry point to the chemical sciences. So, in this section of the book we provide for teachers, or self-learners, the essential chemical background needed to understand the phenomena Faraday touches on in his lectures—see The Big Ideas of Chemistry. *Then following this section we detail six activities and one set of demonstrations teachers can use to help students investigate for themselves "the chemical history of a candle." Each activity has a student version followed by a teacher's guide. These teaching guides and student worksheets can be downloaded at* www.engineerguy. com/faraday.

THE BIG IDEAS OF CHEMISTRY:
THE PARTICULATE NATURE
OF MATTER

In this section we cover the essential ideas that should be shared with younger students in order to better understand the phenomena that Faraday addresses. Our goal here is not rigor, but instead a set of simple analogies that give students an entry point to understanding the particulate nature of matter. We will focus our discussion on the following "big ideas" in chemistry:

- All matter is made of atoms.

- Atoms are in constant motion.

- Atoms can stick together to become a liquid or solid, or bond together to form molecules.

- At normal conditions of temperature and pressure, some substances are solids, some are liquids, and others are gases. This has to do with how attractive ("sticky") the particles (atoms or molecules) are that make up the substance.

- Chemical reactions are the result of a rearrangement of atoms.

Atomic viewpoint essential to modern science

The importance of the particulate nature of matter cannot be overstated. Nobel Prize-winning physicist Richard Feynman once asked "if all scientific knowledge were lost in a cataclysm, what single statement would preserve the most information for the next generation of creatures?" He proposed the following:

> All things are made of atoms—little particles that move around in perpetual motion, attracting each other when they are a little distance apart, but repelling upon being squeezed together. In that one sentence, you will see, there is an enormous amount of information about the world, if just a little imagination and thinking are applied.

For many young students this notion of a microscopic world is too abstract to grasp, so it is often best to start with a rough analogy that shows how a commonplace object is built of small units. For example, a beach looks from afar as though it were a solid surface, yet when examined up close the individual particles of sand can be distinguished. Once this analogy is firm in student's minds, one should ask them to think about a chemical familiar to them: water. Explain that just as small pieces of sand comprise a beach, water is made of small molecules,which are composed of two hydrogen (H) atoms and one oxygen (O) atom. (See figure on next page.)

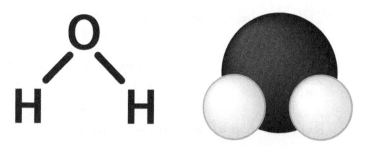

While the molecules that make up water are, as are all molecules, too small to see with the naked eye or even ordinary microscopes—scientists use a "scanning tunneling microscope" to image atoms and molecules—everyday observations support the idea of a particulate nature of matter.

Helping students "see" atoms in everyday life

With a little guidance students can "see" the effects of the particulate nature of matter. For example, the smells created by cooking waft through the house. The spreading of these aromas suggests that the molecules reach the olfactory sensors in our noses by floating through the air. Next, using another kitchen-based analogy, you can demonstrate the effects of the particulate theory: add a drop or two of food coloring to water, taking care to avoid disturbing it. Ask students to note the movement of the food coloring: it spreads in *all* directions. The food coloring does not simply "fall" through the water due to gravity, but its spreads sideways, and even ascends in the water so that, given time, the entire sample of water becomes colored. This observation suggests to students that the water molecules in the glass constantly move and that they move randomly. These moving water molecules, over time, "shove" the food coloring molecules to all sections of the glass until the water has a uniform color.

Relationship of motion to temperature

The diffusion of food coloring in water can next be used to introduce students to the idea that temperature is related to the motion of atoms or molecules. If students observe the diffusion of food coloring in hot and cold water they will note that the food coloring spreads more quickly in the hot water. Based on our analogy of moving water molecules spreading the food color, this implies that the water molecules in the hotter water move more quickly than the water molecules in the cold water. You can then explain with more precision the scientific basis of temperature: temperature is a measure of the average kinetic energy (motion) of the molecules or atoms.

Physical changes versus chemical changes

A key concept in Faraday's lectures is the distinction between a physical and a chemical change. You can introduce students to a physical change by studying a sugar-water solution, and then to a chemical change with the electrolysis of water.

Physical changes

Ask students to dissolve sugar in water. Just as with the food coloring, students can use their senses to detect that the sugar dissolves and spreads through the water, this time, though, by taste. As with the food coloring, the moving water molecules disperse sugar molecules until they are distributed throughout the water. Next, have students either heat the solution and boil away the water, or let the solution sit overnight until the water evaporates. Either process will leave a residue of sugar. To effect either of these processes the liquid water must become a vapor. Note that the molecules (H_2O) are the same in both the liquid and vaporous states. The sugar molecules, as well, are the same whether sugar is a solid or is dissolved in water. Because the molecules stay intact this is called a *physical* change as opposed to a *chemical change*, as described in the next section.

Knowing that temperature increases molecular motion helps students to understand this phase change from liquid to vapor. In its liquid state the water molecules are attracted to one another and are touching, yet able to move past one another; that is, they are able to flow. When we add energy by heating, the water molecules move faster and travel further until their attraction for one another is overcome and they begin to separate. Students can see this when water boils: the vapor exits as bubbles. These bubbles are made because water molecules are separating from one another

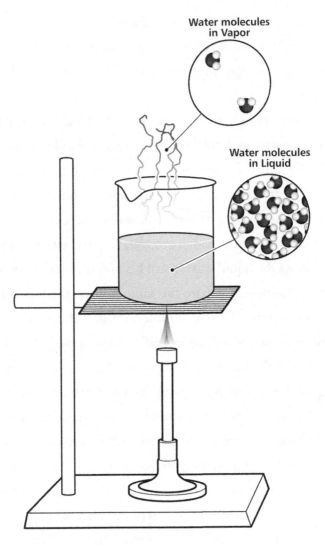

Water molecules in Vapor

Water molecules in Liquid

and spreading out. As the bubbles reach the surface of the water, the fast moving water molecules escape into the air.

We can reverse this process and lower the temperature of liquid water. In this case the motion of the water molecules slows down. The attractive forces between the molecules and the slower moving molecules result in ice, which is, of course, a solid. In the ice the molecules are still moving by vibrating, but they are no longer able to move past one another. The freezing of water, like the boiling of water, is a physical change because the molecules remain intact.

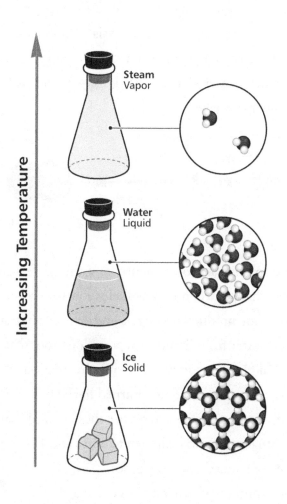

Chemical changes

While the molecules remain the same in a physical change, the same is not true for a chemical change. Passing an electric current through water produces hydrogen and oxygen gases. This is a chemical change because a substance is turned into something chemically different—in this case into two substances. The electrolysis of water highlights the profundity of a chemical change: water can put out a fire, yet the two products created, oxygen and hydrogen, are highly flammable.

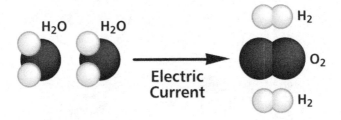

Be sure to contrast for students how this differs from a physical change: when they boiled water to recover sugar they did not produce hydrogen and oxygen, but simply changed water from liquid to vapor. Note, too, that often a physical change is easily reversible by another physical process: water vapor can be returned to the liquid state by condensation. In contrast, to reverse the chemical change of water into oxygen and hydrogen requires another chemical change—we must ignite the gases.

Determining whether a physical or a chemical change takes place is often difficult for students. So, students find useful a few heuristics or clues that help them decide whether an event is a physical or a chemical change. The hallmark of a chemical change is a chemically new product and so often the result is a color change, an evolution of gas, emission of heat, or the formation of a solid.

Cohesion & adhesion:
Intermolecular attraction

In a chemical change molecules broke apart and rearranged into other chemical species—that is, a bond was broken. In contrast to this *intra*molecular change, physical changes are controlled by *inter*molecular forces—the much weaker forces that cause molecules to be attracted or repelled to each other. The degree of attraction determines whether a substance is solid, liquid or gas at a particular temperature and pressure. For example, at room temperature and pressure oxygen exists as a gas, water as a liquid, and sugar as a solid. The existence of these chemically pure species as solids, liquids and gases at room temperature reveals to students that the attraction among molecules varies.

These differing amounts of attraction account for some common everyday observations. Open a bottle of fingernail polish remover, which is a mixture of acetone and water, and in a few minutes the odor of acetone fills the room. The acetone molecules in the remover are attracted to one another enough to be a liquid when the bottle is closed, but the acetone turns into a vapor because it evaporates quicker than water. This happens because water molecules attract each other more than do acetone molecules. The reason has to do with the structure of the atoms and the shapes of molecules, but for students at this stage it is enough to know that while molecules attract one another, they do so with varying degrees. For example, ask students to observe a drop of water and a drop of acetone on a clean glass slide. The water droplet will be larger than the acetone droplet because the surface tension of water is higher than for acetone. This occurs because water molecules are more strongly attracted to one another than acetone molecules are to each other.

The force that holds like molecules together is called *cohesion* while the force holding unlike molecules together is called *adhesion*. The interplay of these two forces results in the phenomenon of capillary action, which students will learn about in one of the activities described in the next section (and which is discussed in Lecture One). We can see the effects of cohesion and adhesion in a mixture of oil and water. These two substance do not mix readily, and even when shaken they separate into oil and water phases. This is not because water molecules and oil molecules repel one another, but partly because the water molecules stick together and the oil molecules stick together. That is, the force of cohesion of the water molecules and the force of cohesion of the oil molecules is greater than the force of adhesion for an oil and water molecule.

TABLE OF CONTENTS TO
STUDENT ACTIVITIES
& DEMONSTRATIONS
WITH TEACHING GUIDES

Observations of a Candle • 137
Teacher's Guide • 141

Convection Currents & Density • 147
Teacher's Guide • 151

Capillary Action • 155
Teacher's Guide • 159

Molecules are "Sticky" • 161
Teacher's Guide • 167

Physical Changes: Changes of State • 171
Teacher's Guide • 179

Chemical Changes • 183
Teacher's Guide • 185

Two Demonstrations to Show
the Pressure Caused by Air • 187

OBSERVATIONS OF A CANDLE

Science is one way we have to try to better understand the world around us. We sometimes start by asking questions, such as, "I wonder what clouds are made of?", or "I wonder why the sky is blue?" To answer these questions we make careful observations. Observing is not just "seeing" but paying careful attention to details. It is important to write down these observations because it is easy to overlook or forget them. We can use these observations to develop theories or explanations of *why* something is the way that it is. With incorrect or missing observations, our theories are more likely to be incorrect.

Today, you will observe some candles. Your goals are to:

- Write as much detail as you can about what a candle looks like before it is lit, while it is lit, and after you blow out the flame.

- Ask questions and try to design and carry out experiments to answer these questions.

- Try to better understand how a candle works.

Part one: The unlit candle

Describe the candle as completely as you can. Make sure to answer the following questions:

- What color is the candle?

- How big is the candle?

- What shape is the candle?

- What does the wick look like?

Part two: The lit candle

Light the wick of the candle or have your teacher do it for you and then answer the following questions about the flame of the candle. Pictures would help your answers.

- How big is the flame?

- What is the shape of the flame?

- What color(s) do you notice in the flame?

- Is the flame brighter in some areas more than others?

Also, provide answers for each of the following:

- Do you see any smoke coming from the candle?

- Describe what is happening to the wax of the candle.

- Describe what is happening to the wick of the candle.

Part three: The blown-out candle

Carefully blow out the flame. Describe what you see. Pay attention to any smoke, the wick, and the wax of the candle. Answer the following questions:

- How does the candle and wick differ from before the candle was lit?

- How are they the same?

Part four: Developing questions to experiment with the candle

Work with a partner and come up with questions and experiments you can do with the candle. For example, "what happens if you cover the lit candle with a glass?" Once you have some questions, talk them over with your teacher and classmates and develop a list of questions for the class to answer.

Part five: Experimenting with the candle

With the permission of your teacher, carry out your experiments and make sure to take detailed notes about what you observe. Share your results with the class.

OBSERVATIONS OF A CANDLE
Teacher's Guide

Observing a candle is a great way to get students to think about science as a process of better understanding the world around them. Most likely, they have all looked at candles, but they may not have really observed them. Explain to your students that observing is not just "seeing" but paying careful attention to details. We can use these observations to develop theories or explanations of *why* something is the way that it is. With incorrect or missing observations, our theories are more likely to be incorrect.

Provide as many different types of candles as you can for the students (birthday candles, tea lights, votive candles, etc.) and have them make observations before a candle is lit, while it is lit, and after the flame has been blown out. Students should focus on the wick, the wax, the flame, and the smoke. Note, for example, that the wick blackens after it is lit. The flame has a triangular shape and does not seem to touch the wax but appears to "float" above it. The flame is also blue closer to the wick, and yellow above it, with the brightest part of the flame being in the center. Most likely, little, if any, smoke is given off as it burns, and only appears after the flame is extinguished. The wax melts nearest to the flame, and "cups" may form depending on the shape of the initial candle. There may be "guttering" as Faraday calls it, or drips of wax down the side of the candle without these cups. These observations are made by Faraday and they will be more understandable and the lectures will be more engaging if the students note these before viewing the lectures.

Throughout the lectures, Faraday asks questions (such as "How does the flame get hold of the fuel?") and then proceeds to answer these questions by performing demonstrations coupled with explanations. This activity will have the students model this approach and you can make this explicit as they are watching the lectures. You will need glasses of some sort to cover the candles.

Observations of the unlit candle

These will vary depending on the candle used.

Observations of the lit candle

When the candle is lit, the students should notice that the flame is a triangular (conical) shape (depending on how still the air is in the room—it is best to observe when still). The outer part of the flame appears blue (especially at the bottom nearest the wax) and the part of the flame immediately surrounding the wick is a grayish yellow color. The middle part of the flame is the brightest (yellow).

The wick burns quickly (blackens) until it gets closer to the candle wax. The flame does not touch the top of the candle. The tip of the wick glows.

The wax at the top of the candle is turning into a liquid. It may drip down the side of the candle or a "cup" may be formed (depending on the candle).

Very little smoke is generally given off if the candle is burning undisturbed.

The variance in the flame is due to different temperatures and different processes occurring in various parts of the flame (which are discussed in the Lectures and in the Lecture Guides). This does not need to be discussed at this point of the activity unless prompted by student questions.

It would be helpful to draw a flame on the board to show the different colors.

Observations of the blown-out candle

When the candle is blown-out we see smoke. The amount produced depends on the size of the flame.

The wick may be a bit shorter. If you are using a previously burned candle, there will not be much difference in terms of the length sticking out the top if the candle (the wick and candle end up decreasing at the same rate).

The candle will be shorter and perhaps has "trails" of wax down the side.

Questions & experiments

In Part Four we provided a sample question: "What happens if you cover the lit candle with a glass?" It may be helpful to ask this question as a class and have each group try this before developing more questions (this activity may generate more questions, such as those suggested below). Students should notice fogginess on the inside of the glass and that the flame fades and eventually goes out. It is not necessary at this point to tell them that the fogginess is due to water or that the flame goes out from a lack of enough oxygen. The main point of this activity is to ask questions, make observations, and use these to ask more questions of the form "what would happen if?" This will make the material a bit more familiar to them so that the lectures make more sense.

If the students are struggling coming up with questions, you can follow-up with the suggested question on page 139: "Try this again, but before the flame goes out, lift the glass. What happens?"

In this case the flame will become brighter once the glass is lifted (due to the increase in available oxygen).

Have the students develop other tests and come up with other questions. For now, you can decide how much to explain, but again, it is a good idea to give the students some time to explore without being asked to explain at this point. Have them make careful observations, test different variables, and ask questions.

If students are struggling to come up with tests, you may wish to suggest these:

- What happens if you put two lit candles under the glass? Do they both go out at the same time? Do they go out more quickly, less quickly, or in the same amount of time as one candle? Does it matter if one candle is taller than the other?

- What happens if you cover the flame to put it out, relight, and then cover it with the same glass? Is it different if you use a fresh glass? Have the students cover a flame with a glass, let the flame go out, and then take off the glass and place it mouth side down on the table. Relight, and recover with the glass. See what happens to the time it takes to go out as you continue to do this.

- Does the size of the glass affect how long it takes for a candle to go out?

If you are willing and able, students will most likely want to replicate what Faraday discusses and try to blow out the flame and try to re-light it by igniting the smoke. There is some technique in doing this—you must blow the flame gently (Faraday uses the word "cleverly" in the original text) and there needs to be a fair amount of smoke coming from the wick. Light the smoke while the trail is relatively thick and reaches the wick. With practice, and the right conditions of the smoke, you can re-light the candle a few inches from the wick.

CONVECTION CURRENTS
& DENSITY

Use scissors to cut the design on the next page by cutting all of the lines. You will be able to hold what is the middle of the circle and the cut paper will form a spiral. Poke a small hole in the top of the spiral and connect a length of thread so that you can hold the thread and let the spiral hang freely. Does the spiral spin if you dangle it in the air?

Next, light a candle and hold the center of the spiral above the flame of the candle. Be careful that the paper does not touch the flame. What happens now? Does the spiral spin?

Move the spiral from the candle or blow out the candle. What happens? Can you explain your observations?

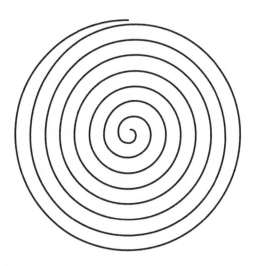

CONVECTION CURRENTS
& DENSITY
Teacher's Guide

Background. The characteristic triangular or conical shape of the flame is due to the convection currents. The heat of the flame causes the air directly around the flame (and carbon dioxide and water vapor products) to expand making these gases less dense. This draws in relatively cool air from below which pushes up the hotter gases and gives the shape to the flame.

If we place a flame in space (such as in a space shuttle), thus removing gravity as a factor, we no longer get these convection currents. The flame becomes more spherical, and, because the oxygen spends a longer time in the flame, there is more complete combustion. The yellow color gives way to blue because we do not have the "free carbon particles" glowing in the flame producing the bright light. The flame also does not last very long because, without convection currents, carbon dioxide is not carried away and it smothers the flame.

We can see the same phenomenon in a vacuum chamber. By removing air (but keeping enough oxygen to burn), we remove the convection currents and we see the same short-lived spherical blue flame as in space.

Details of the Student Activity. Have students cut out the spiral design; be sure that they cut along the line of the spiral: when they hold the center of the circle the paper will form a conical spiral. Students should poke a small hole in the top of the spiral and connect a length of thread so that they can hold the thread and allow the spiral to hang freely.

Show the students that if you hold the thread the spiral will not spin.

Next, light a candle and hold the center of the spiral above the flame of the candle. Be careful that the paper does not touch the flame. After a few seconds the spiral will start to spin.

Students can then either move the spiral from the candle or blow out the candle and the spiral will stop spinning after a few seconds.

This happens because heat from the candle flame is transferred to the air. The hot air is less dense than the room temperature air, and the hot air rises. Room temperature air moves in to fill this space, and this air is then heated and rises. This motion of the air goes through the spiral and makes it move.

This same current also gives the flame its triangular shape and also causes cooler room air to go up the sides of the candle to cool the wax. This allows the candle to keep its shape even though the heat is melting the wax on the inside of the candle.

Extension: Convection currents in water

For this demonstration you will show convection currents in water instead of air, and you will also dramatically show the difference in density between hot and cold water. You will need:

- Four identical bottles (it is crucial that the mouths be exactly the same size)

- Hot and cold water

- Food coloring (blue and yellow work well)

- An index card or playing card

Add a few drops (depending on the size of the bottle) of blue food coloring to each of two of the bottles, and a few drops of yellow food coloring to the other two bottles. Add warm water (tap water is fine—make it as warm as you can hold) to two of the bottles (so that the warm water is the same color) and cold water to the other two bottles. Cooling the water in a refrigerator or with ice is preferable to cold tap water (the bigger the difference in temperatures between the hot and cold water, the better). Make sure that the bottles are filled to the very top with water.

First, place the card over the mouth of one of the bottles with warm water. Hold the card and turn the bottle upside down over the bottle with cold water. Position the bottles so that they are mouth-to-mouth. While holding the bottles (you may use an assistant) carefully pull the card from between the bottles. If done carefully there will be very little mixing of the water (you may see a bit of green where the hot water meets the cold water) because the hot water is less dense that the cold water. Thus, the cold water stays in the bottom bottle and the hot water stays in the top bottle.

Next, repeat the demonstration but place the cold water on top of the hot water. In this case the cold water will sink and the hot water will rise and the two samples will mix, resulting in green water in both bottles.

CAPILLARY ACTION

In the candle the molten wax rise up the wick by capillary action, which is demonstrated in the activities described here.

Moving water from one beaker to another

1. Get two drinking glasses, a stirring rod, a piece of paper towel, and blue and yellow food coloring.

2. Fill one of the drinking glasses with almost a cup of water, add 10 drops of blue food coloring to the water, and stir. Add a cup of water and ten drops of yellow food coloring to the other glass.

3. Take the piece of paper towel and twist it to make something that resembles a rope.

4. Place one end of the paper towel rope into the beaker with the blue water. Watch what happens to the water. Bend the rope and place the other end into the other glass (with the yellow food coloring).

5. Watch this for a couple of minutes and observe what is happening. Over the course of an hour continue with other activities, and return to this from time to time.

Moving water up celery

1. Get a drinking glass, a stalk of celery, a knife, and food coloring.

2. Put about a ¼ cup of water into the glass, add 10 drops of red or blue food coloring in the water, and stir.

3. Cut off a bit of each end of the celery stalk.

4. Place a freshly cut end of the celery stalk into the colored water.

5. Let this sit while you do the other activities and return to this from time to time.

Blooming flowers

1. Color and cut out a paper flower on the next page and then fold the petals. Work with someone else and fold the petals differently. Perhaps one person can fold them one by one in order, and another in a different order.

2. Use the dropper to add a little water to the center of a flat dish.

3. Drop the flower with the folded petals into the middle of the water. Watch what happens.

4. What happens?

5. Why does this happen?

CAPILLARY ACTION
Teacher's Guide

In Lecture One Faraday tells us that capillary action is responsible for transporting the melted candle wax up the wick and to the flame. He also shows us another common example of capillary action—that of water traveling up a towel that is hanging in a basin of water.

As we discussed in *The Big Ideas of Chemistry,* molecules are attracted to one another. Capillary action is due to the adhesion of the molecules of a liquid with the molecules in the surrounding solid (the towel, for example). Since the water molecules are also attracted to each other (cohesion) the water appears to climb. This occurs in a candle wick as the candle wax is heated until it is molten (a liquid) and the liquid wax "climbs" the wick. The fact that a wick allows for capillary action is the reason why sportswear that is meant to keep us dry is said to be "wicking."

Plants also use capillary action to transport water from the soil, through the roots, and throughout the plant.

We have included three activities for students to explore capillary action. The activities with the paper towel and the celery take thirty minutes of so for results, so you may wish to have the students set them up at the beginning of class time.

MOLECULES ARE "STICKY"

Part one: How many drops of H_2O can fit on a penny?

You are going to see how many drops of water you can add to a penny before the water runs off of the penny.

First of all, make a guess: how many drops of water do you think will fit on the penny?

My guess is _____

Water drops on a penny

1. Rinse a penny in tap water and dry completely.

2. Place the penny on a paper towel.

3. Use a dropper to place drops of water on the penny (one at a time) until *any* amount of water runs over the edge of the penny.

4. Record the number of drops for that trial in the table on the next page.

5. Repeat Steps 1–4 once more and calculate the average. Record this in the table on the next page.

NUMBER OF WATER DROPS ON A PENNY

trial #1	trial #2	average

Part two: Hanging drops of water

How big is your drop?

1. Get a glass, a dropper, and wax paper that has been taped to a piece of cardboard. Fill the cup with water.

2. Squeeze the bulb of the pipet and place the tip under water. Allow the bulb to expand to fill the pipet with water.

3. Over the plastic sheet, see how large of a water drop you can make without letting the water drop fall from the pipet. Compare your drop to those of the others in the class. Make a sketch of the water drop coming out of the pipet.

Touching water

1. Place a drop of water on a piece of wax paper taped to cardboard.

2. Gently touch the tip of the pipet to the top of the drop of water. What happens?

3. Gently squeeze the pipet so a water drop hangs from the pipet (like in Part One above) and touch this drop to the top of the water drop on the wax paper. What happens?

Part three: Moving water

Moving water by pulling

1. Place several drops of water on the wax paper.

2. Gently touch the tip of the pipet to the side of one of the drops and pull the water drop until it touches another drop. What happens?

3. Use the pipet to drag all of the drops of water together. When you have a large water drop, try to pull it with the pipet. What happens? If you can still pull the water drop, keep adding water until you can no longer pull the drop. What happens when you try to pull it?

Moving water by tilting

1. Get the large drop of water in the middle of the wax paper on the cardboard.

2. Tilt the cardboard so that the water drop moves. Try to get the drop as close to the edge as possible without falling off, and then back to the middle. Practice until you feel comfortable that you can control the drop.

Part four: Water vs. alcohol: which is "stickier"?

Alcohol drops on a penny

1. Rinse a penny in tap water and dry completely.

2. Place the penny on a paper towel.

3. Use a dropper to place drops of alcohol on the penny (one at a time) until *any* amount of alcohol runs over the edge of the penny.

4. Record the number of drops for that trial in the table on the next page.

5. Repeat Steps 1–4 once more and calculate the average. Record this in the table on the next page.

NUMBER OF ALCOHOL DROPS ON A PENNY

trial #	trial #2	average

Comparing drops

1. Make as tall a drop of water as possible on the piece of wax paper (keep adding drops and look at it from the side until it is not getting taller).

2. Make as tall a drop of alcohol as possible on the piece of wax paper (keep adding drops and look at it from the side until it is not getting taller).

3. Draw a picture below of each from the side showing which is taller. Label the drops.

(wax paper)

Questions

Which molecules are "stickier": water molecules or alcohol molecules? How do you know?

MOLECULES ARE "STICKY"
Teacher's Guide

Part one: How many drops of H_2O can fit on a penny

The guess and actual number of water drops on a penny will vary. Students generally guess a number smaller than the actual and are quite surprised by how many drops of water they can fit on a penny. The average value is the sum of the two values divided by 2.

Part two: How big is your drop?

Students are generally surprised as well how big of a drop of water can hang from a dropper—the surface tension of water is greater than they imagine.

Touching water

The water drop will "bead up" on the wax paper, that is, it will not lie flat. It will form what looks like a ball. When the pipet touches the water, the plastic of the pipet will attract the water and "tug" at the drop (students will pull the water drops in the next section). When a drop of water from the pipet is touched to the drop of water on the wax paper, the water from the pipet will generally be pulled into the water drop to form a larger drop (aided by gravity).

Part three: Moving water by pulling

As seen in the previous section, the pipet will stick to the water drop. If the water drop is small enough, it can be pulled by the pipet. If the water drop is too large, it is possible to pull a smaller drop from the larger drop.

Moving water by tilting

Since a water molecule is much more attracted to another water molecule than the wax, we see "beading up" of the water, and so the water drop will easily glide over the wax paper.

Part four: Alcohol drops on a penny *&* comparing drops

Students will find that alcohol molecules are not as "sticky" as water molecules. They will be able to fit much fewer drops of alcohol than water on a penny, and the height of a drop of alcohol will be less than the height of the water drop.

Extension: Water down a string demo

1. Have two students perform this under your direction or get one student volunteer to work with you.

2. You will need two plastic cups. Add a cup of water to one of them. Also get a piece of wet string.

3. One person should hold one end of the string into the empty cup.

4. The other person should hold the other end of the string over the rim of the cup with water. Lift the cup with water and hold the cups far enough apart so that the string is tight.

5. Your goal is to pour as much of the water as possible down the string into the empty cup.

6. Ask the students: "Why were you able to pour water down the string?" Because water molecules attract one another, once the strong is wet (due to capillary action), the water that your pour from one cup "sticks" to the water that is in the string.

PHYSICAL CHANGES:
CHANGES OF STATE

Matter generally exists in three states or phases: solid, liquid, or gas. We can change the state in a variety of ways and this usually, but not always, involves heat in some way. When a substance undergoes a change of state or a phase change, we consider it a physical change because the molecules that make up that substance are not changed (which is different from a chemical change).

Solids have their own shape, while liquids and gases take the shape of their container. Solids and liquids have definite volumes, but a gas expands to fill the volume of its container. It is important to consider the molecules making up the solid, liquid, or gas when considering the difference among these states.

Before we begin the lab, show the differences among a solid, liquid, and gas using circles to represent molecules and then explain your sketches.

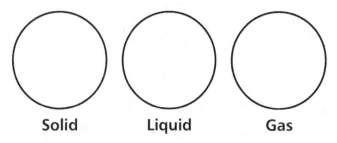

Solid   **Liquid**   **Gas**

Changes between any two states in any direction are possible. Name as many of these processes as you can and place your answers in the table below. We will discuss ones you do not know.

Process	Name of Phase Change
solid to liquid	
liquid to solid	
liquid to gas	
gas to liquid	
solid to gas	
gas to solid	

In chemistry, we also write these changes in the form of an equation. For example, suppose solid "A" is heated until it turns into a liquid. We say that solid A melted to form liquid A, and we can represent this as:

$$A(s) \rightarrow A(l)$$

The arrow shows that a transformation has occurred. We use (s) to designate a solid, (l) for liquid, and (g) for gas.

In order for a change of state to occur, energy is either required or released. Let's look at two samples of H_2O, one liquid and one solid.

Add about 200–250 mL of $H_2O(l)$ to one 400-mL beaker, and about 200–250 mL of $H_2O(s)$ to another 400-mL beaker.

Place each on a hotplate and use a thermometer to determine the temperature of each. Make sure to take the temperature in the middle of each of the samples. Record these temperatures in the table on the next page.

Turn the hotplate to the highest setting and start the timer. Record the temperatures at every 1 minute interval, making sure to take the temperature in the middles of the samples, and making sure to carefully stir the samples. Record the temperatures in the table on the next page.

	Temperature of $H_2O(l)$	Temperature of $H_2O(s)$
initial		
1 minute		
2 minutes		
3 minutes		
4 minutes		
5 minutes		
6 minutes		
7 minutes		
8 minutes		
9 minutes		
10 minutes		

Explain your results for both $H_2O(l)$ and $H_2O(s)$.

Water as liquid & vapor

Add 150 mL water to a 400-mL beaker. Put the beaker on a hot plate and bring the water to a boil. Take the beaker off of the hotplate. Place a watch glass over the beaker. Make observations inside and outside of the beaker, along with on the top and bottom of the watch glass. Remove and add the watch glass to the beaker a few times. Write down any observations.

1. What change(s) occurs in the beaker? Describe, name, and write an equation for the change or changes.

2. What change(s) occurs on the top of the watch glass? Describe, name, and write an equation for the change or changes.

Water as solid, liquid, & vapor

1. Add some ice to the top of the watch glass when it is on the beaker. Record observations.

2. What change(s) occurs on the bottom of the watch glass? Describe, name, and write an equation for the change or changes.

3. Add a few drops of food coloring to the water and bring the water to boiling. Take the beaker off of the hot plate, place a watch glass over the beaker, and some ice on the watch glass. Record observations, specifically at the bottom of the watch glass.

Variation: Water as a liquid & vapor

You will need:

- Two clear plastic cups—one with a wide mouth, and one with a smaller mouth. The small-mouth cup should fit upside down in the wide-mouth as in the figure on the next page.

- Hot water

Procedure

1. Fill a wide-mouth cup about ½ full of hot water.

2. Place the small-mouth cup upside down inside the other cup as shown below.

3. Observe the cups. Pay attention to the inside of the cups. Do you see anything?

4. After about 2–3 minutes, remove the top cup and feel the inside. What do you notice?

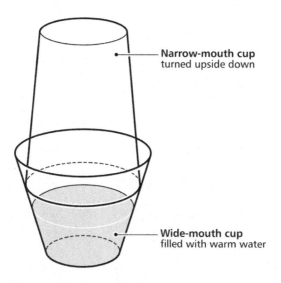

Narrow-mouth cup
turned upside down

Wide-mouth cup
filled with warm water

PHYSICAL CHANGES:
CHANGES OF STATE
Teacher's Guide

The diagrams will vary but should look like those of ice, liquid water, and steam in the *Big Ideas* section.

Process	Name of Phase Change
solid to liquid	melting
liquid to solid	freezing
liquid to gas	vaporizing
gas to liquid	condensation
solid to gas	sublimation
gas to solid	deposition

For heating water, actual temperatures over time will vary (but always increase) but you will notice that the temperature of ice will remain constant until the ice is melted. For the demonstration using the hotplate the glassware *must* be Pyrex because glass cannot withstand the heat and will shatter. The heat added to liquid water is making the molecules move more rapidly and temperature is a measure of kinetic energy (or energy of motion). For ice, the heat is used to break the forces holding the molecules together as a liquid, so the temperature doesn't change until the water molecules are able to move freely (flow).

Water as a solid, liquid, & vapor

Students should notice fogginess in the beaker, with liquid water collecting on the underside of the watch glass, and possibly near the top of the inside of the beaker. When ice is added to the watch glass, students will notice the ice melt and also notice faster accumulation of water on the underside of the watch glass and larger drops of water. Removing the watch glass will result in the water "disappearing" (less foggy) and replacing the watch glass will result in the reappearance of the water.

Students will see both evaporation

$$H_2O(l) \rightarrow H_2O(g)$$

and condensation

$$H_2O(g) \rightarrow H_2O(l)$$

of water, along with the melting

$$H_2O(s) \rightarrow H_2O(l)$$

of ice.

When food coloring is added to the water many students might think that colored water will appear on the underside of the watch glass. The food coloring does not evaporate, however, and so does not appear on the watch glass. This is a simple distillation of water.

The variation with the plastic cups is useful depending on your supplies. You can also add ice to the top of the upper cup, and use food coloring.

CHEMICAL CHANGES

Physical change or chemical change?

1. You will need two plastic cups, two ¼-cup measuring cups, and a spoon.

2. Add a spoonful of baking soda to each beaker (add the same amount to each beaker—as close as you can make it).

3. Measure ¼ cup of water and ¼ cup of vinegar.

4. Add the water to one cup and the vinegar to the other cup.

5. Record your observations.

Question 1: In one of these cups there was a physical change and in the other there was a chemical change. Which was which? How can you tell?

Question 2: In general, what are four clues that a chemical reaction has occurred?

Baking soda & vinegar

Part one: Collecting the gas

1. You will need a small water bottle, one ¼-cup measuring cup, a balloon, a funnel, and a spoon.

2.   Add a spoonful of baking soda to the balloon using the funnel.

3.   Pour ¼ cup of vinegar into the bottle.

4.   Fix the balloon to the mouth of the bottle.

5.   Lift the balloon and allow the baking soda to go into the bottle.

6.   Record your observations. Draw a picture before, during, and after the reaction.

Part two: Testing the gas

1.   Add a spoonful of baking soda to a plastic cup.

2.   Pour ¼ cup of vinegar into the beaker.

3.   Place a flaming splint into the beaker. What happens?

4.   How can you tell that carbon dioxide gas was a product of the reaction?

Baking soda & vinegar

1.   Measure ¼ cup of vinegar into a plastic cup. Measure the temperature of the vinegar.

2.   Add a teaspoon of baking soda to vinegar.

3.   Write down your observations. Record the temperature of the solution.

4.   Was this a chemical reaction? How can you tell? What clues were there?

CHEMICAL CHANGES
Teacher's Guide

Physical change or chemical change?

When vinegar is added to the baking soda, students should notice the evolution of bubbles and the "disappearance" of at least some baking soda (depending on the relative amounts that are added). This is because there is a chemical change between baking soda and vinegar, resulting in the formation of a gas (carbon dioxide).

When water is added to the baking soda, no bubbles form and the water becomes cloudy with stirring. Some of the baking soda "disappears" as it dissolves in the water (but not to a great extent). This is a physical change.

Four clues that a chemical reaction has occurred are: formation of gas, formation of a solid, color change, and change in temperature.

Baking soda & vinegar

Carbon dioxide is produced by the reaction of baking soda and vinegar. While it is an invisible gas, students can observe its presence in a couple of ways. They will first collect it in a balloon and notice the increase in volume and pressure in the balloon. Next, they will test the gas with the flaming splint. Since carbon dioxide cannot support combustion (as Michael Faraday shows us), the flame will be extinguished when placed in an atmosphere of carbon dioxide. Since the mixing of baking soda and vinegar produced a gas with new properties, we can say this is a chemical reaction.

We can also see this is a chemical reaction by measuring the temperature of the vinegar before and after it reacts with the baking soda. Students should note that the temperature goes down. A temperature change is another clue of a chemical reaction.

Variations

You can also vary this by using solutions of Epsom salts (magnesium sulfate) and washing soda (sodium carbonate). You can dissolve a bit of each in water. When mixed, a solid forms (magnesium carbonate) and the temperature goes down.

Mixing baking soda into a solution of calcium chloride results in the formation of a solid (calcium carbonate), the formation of a gas (carbon dioxide), and an increase in temperature. Calcium chloride can be found commercially (such as in home improvement stores) as it is used in products such as DampRid™ and in products for snow removal.

TWO DEMONSTRATIONS
TO SHOW THE PRESSURE
CAUSED BY AIR

Demonstration one: Can crushing

In Lecture Four Michael Faraday boils a bit of water in a metal vessel to fill it with steam, removes it from the heat and seals the bottle. When the steam condenses back to a liquid, a partial vacuum is created and the air pressure crushes the bottle.

You can do a variation of this demonstration by using aluminum soft drink cans. Add a little water to an otherwise empty can and get the water to boil (you need to see a good amount of steam coming out of the top to ensure that the can is filled with steam and most of the air has been pushed out). Using a hot pad, very quickly pick up the can and invert it into a bowl of cold water. The can will be instantly, and dramatically, crushed.

Similarly to Faraday's demonstration, the steam condenses creating a partial vacuum. In this case, a good amount of water is also pushed into the can by air pressure, but because the aluminum is so thin, and the opening of the can is relatively small, the water cannot rush into the can quickly enough and the can is crushed by atmospheric pressure.

Demonstration two: Egg in a bottle

For this demonstration you will need a peeled hard-boiled egg, matches or a lighter, a piece of paper, and a glass bottle which has a mouth slightly smaller than the egg. Be sure to cover the bottle in transparent tape because the decreased pressure can cause the bottle to implode.

Set the piece of paper on fire and drop the burning paper into the bottle. Before the flame goes out, place the peeled hard-boiled egg on the mouth of the bottle. You may notice the egg "bounce" a couple of times and the egg is then forced into the bottle.

A common misconception is that the pressure decreases in the bottle due solely to the fact that oxygen gas is "used up" in burning. But as Faraday shows us, carbon dioxide gas is a product of combustion. While there is generally less carbon dioxide produced (by volume) than oxygen gas reacted, this does not by itself account for the difference in pressure.

By heating the air in the bottle, the molecules in the air move more quickly and farther apart from one another. Some of the molecules escape the bottle (which is why you may see the egg "bounce"). When the flame goes out, the air cools back to room temperature, but there is now less air in the bottle than before because the egg is blocking the air from returning. Thus, the air pressure outside the bottle is greater than the air pressure inside the bottle. The higher pressure pushes the egg into the bottle.

The egg can be removed from the bottle by holding the bottle upside down so that the egg is sitting inside the mouth of the bottle. Blow into the bottle and the egg should be pushed out. You will need to make a seal with your lips over the mouth of the bottle—expanding your lungs lowers the pressure, just like using a straw.

This book is set in Adobe Caslon, a superb digital rendering of the typeface designed by the great English type designer William Caslon (1692–1766). Caslon began his career as an engraver of pistols and muskets, eventually moving into letter founding, which brought him fame in his lifetime. He produced every letter carefully, cutting each by hand over a period of twenty years. Some designers take a dim view of this individuality, but despite this professional disdain, the typeface remains one of the best loved. It was used in the printed version of the Declaration of Independence. In the version used here type designer Carol Twombly (1959–) has captured the unique character and charm of this eighteenth-century typeface.

The typeface Mundo Sans graces the page headers. A sans-serif typeface created by Carl Crossgrove, it first appeared in 2002, although he started work on it in 1991. He admired humanist sans typeface like Metro, Formata, Gill, and Syntax. To create Mundo Sans, Crossgrove said he "used these designs—and, surprisingly, Futura—as models for the proportion, weight, flow, spacing and rhythm." He drew inspiration for the heavier weights from traditional hand-lettered signage, with its heavy sans caps, slightly flaring stems, and humanist skeleton. He succeeded admirably in creating a design clean and distinctive enough for display use, while still being understated and suitably proportioned for setting text. It's an understated typeface, but not exactly quiet.